CLASSICS *for*
YOUNG READERS

Editor: John Holdren

Art Director: Steve Godwin

Designer: Jayoung Cho

Illustrators:
Jayoung Cho
John Tenniel
Deborah Wolfe Ltd. (Jerry Dadds, Jim Hays, Rob Kemp, Jeff LeVan,
Graham Parslow, Anton Petrov, Phillip Small, Richard Waldrep)

ISBN: 1-931728-51-8

Printed by Worzalla, Stevens Point, WI, USA, March 2012, Lot 032012

TABLE OF CONTENTS

LESSONS LEARNED: NOT WHAT YOU GET, BUT WHAT YOU GIVE

ANIMALS AND THEIR PEOPLE

LIFE STORIES: CREATIVE LIVES

FAVORITES FROM FAMOUS BOOKS: THE JUNGLE BOOK

A MATTER OF JUSTICE

STORIES FROM THE BIBLE

STORIES OF OUR TIME

POETRY

"TO EVERYTHING THERE IS A SEASON"

STUFF AND NONSENSE

LESSONS LEARNED:

NOT WHAT YOU GET, BUT WHAT YOU GIVE

THE STONE

by Lloyd Alexander

There was a cottager named Maibon, and one day he was driving down the road in his horse and cart when he saw an old man hobbling along, so frail and feeble he doubted the poor soul could go many more steps. Though Maibon offered to take him in the cart, the old man refused; and Maibon went his way home, shaking his head over such a pitiful sight, and said to his wife, Modrona:

"Ah, ah, what a sorry thing it is to have your bones creaking and cracking, and dim eyes, and dull wits. When I think this might come to me, too! A fine, strong-armed, sturdy-legged fellow like me? One day to go tottering and have his teeth rattling in his head and live on porridge like a baby? There's no fate worse in all the world."

"There is," answered Modrona, "and that would be to have neither teeth nor porridge. Get on with you, Maibon, and stop borrowing trouble. Hoe your field or you'll have no crop to harvest, and no food for you, or me, or the little ones."

Sighing and grumbling, Maibon did as his wife bade him. Although the day was fair and cloudless, he took no pleasure in it. His ax blade was notched, the wooden handle splintery; his saw had lost its edge; and his hoe, once shining new, had begun to rust. None of his tools, it seemed to him, cut or chopped or delved as well as they once had done.

---

bade: ordered
delved: dug, as with a shovel

"They're as worn-out as that old codger I saw on the road," Maibon said to himself. He squinted up at the sky. "Even the sun isn't as bright as it used to be and doesn't warm me half as well. It's gone threadbare as my cloak. And no wonder, for it's been there longer than I can remember. Come to think of it, the moon's been looking a little wilted around the edges, too.

"As for me," went on Maibon, in dismay, "I'm in even a worse state. My appetite's faded, especially after meals. Mornings, when I wake, I can hardly keep myself from yawning. And at night, when I go to bed, my eyes are so heavy I can't hold them open. If that's the way things are now, the older I grow, the worse it will be!"

In the midst of his complaining, Maibon glimpsed something bouncing and tossing back and forth beside a fallen tree in a corner of the field. Wondering if one of his piglets had squeezed out of the sty and gone rooting for acorns, Maibon hurried across the turf. Then he dropped his ax and gaped in astonishment.

There, struggling to free his leg, which had been caught under the log, lay a short, thickset figure: a dwarf with red hair bristling in all directions beneath his round, close-fitting leather cap. At the sight of Maibon, the dwarf squeezed shut his bright red eyes and began holding his breath. After a moment the dwarf's face went redder than his hair; his cheeks puffed out and soon turned purple. Then he opened one eye and blinked rapidly at Maibon, who was staring at him, speechless.

---

gaped: stared with one's mouth open

9

"What," snapped the dwarf, "you can still see me?"

"That I can," replied Maibon, more than ever puzzled, "and I can see very well you've got yourself tight as a wedge under that log, and all your kicking only makes it worse."

At this the dwarf blew out his breath and shook his fists. "I can't do it!" he shouted. "No matter how I try! I can't make myself invisible! Everyone in my family can disappear—poof! Gone! Vanished! But not me! Not Doli! Believe me, if I could have done, you never would have found me in such a plight. Worse luck! Well, come on. Don't stand there goggling like an idiot. Help me get loose!"

At this sharp command Maibon began tugging and heaving at the log. Then he stopped, wrinkled his brow, and scratched his head, saying:

"Well, now, just a moment, friend. The way you look, and all your talk about turning yourself invisible—I'm thinking you might be one of the Fair Folk."

"Oh, clever!" Doli retorted. "Oh, brilliant! Great clodhopper! Giant beanpole! Of course I am! What else! Enough gabbling. Get a move on. My leg's going to sleep."

"If a man does the Fair Folk a good turn," cried Maibon, his excitement growing, "it's told they must do one for him."

"I knew sooner or later you'd come round to that," grumbled the dwarf. "That's the way of it with you ham-handed, heavy-footed oafs. Time was, you humans got along well with us. But nowadays you no sooner see a Fair Folk than it's grab, grab, grab! Gobble, gobble, gobble! Grant my wish! Give me this, give me that! As if we had nothing better to do!

---

plight: a difficult situation

"Yes, I'll give you a favor," Doli went on. "That's the rule; I'm obliged to. Now, get on with it."

Hearing this, Maibon pulled and pried and chopped away at the log as fast as he could and soon freed the dwarf.

Doli heaved a sigh of relief, rubbed his shin, and cocked a red eye at Maibon, saying:

"All right. You've done your work; you'll have your reward. What do you want? Gold, I suppose. That's the usual. Jewels? Fine clothes? Take my advice, go for something practical. A hazelwood twig to help you find water if your well ever goes dry? An ax that never needs sharpening? A cook pot always brimming with food?"

"None of those!" cried Maibon. He bent down to the dwarf and whispered eagerly, "But I've heard tell that you Fair Folk have magic stones that can keep a man young forever. That's what I want. I claim one for my reward."

Doli snorted. "I might have known you'd pick something like that. As to be expected, you humans have it all muddled. There's nothing can make a man young again. That's even beyond the best of our skills. Those stones you're babbling about? Well, yes, there are such things. But greatly overrated. All they'll do is keep you from growing any older."

"Just as good!" Maibon exclaimed. "I want no more than that!"

Doli hesitated and frowned. "Ah—between the two of us, take the cook pot. Better all around. Those stones—we'd sooner not give them away. There's a difficulty—"

"Because you'd rather keep them for yourselves," Maibon broke in. "No, no, you shan't cheat me of my due. Don't put me off with excuses. I told you what I want, and that's what I'll have. Come, hand it over and not another word."

---

obliged: required
muddled: mixed up; confused

Doli shrugged and opened a leather pouch that hung from his belt. He spilled a number of brightly colored pebbles into his palm, picked out one of the larger stones, and handed it to Maibon. The dwarf then jumped up, took to his heels, raced across the field, and disappeared into a thicket.

Laughing and crowing over his good fortune and his cleverness, Maibon hurried back to the cottage. There he told his wife what had happened and showed her the stone he had claimed from the Fair Folk.

"As I am now, so I'll always be!" Maibon declared, flexing his arms and thumping his chest. "A fine figure of a man! Oho, no gray beard and wrinkled brow for me!"

Instead of sharing her husband's jubilation, Modrona flung up her hands and burst out:

"Maibon, you're a greater fool than ever I supposed! And selfish into the bargain! You've turned down treasures! You didn't even ask that dwarf for so much as new jackets for the children! Nor a new apron for me! You could have had the roof mended. Or the walls plastered. No, a stone is what you ask for! A bit of rock no better than you'll dig up in the cow pasture!"

Crestfallen and sheepish, Maibon began thinking his wife was right and the dwarf had indeed given him no more than a common fieldstone.

"Eh, well, it's true," he stammered; "I feel no different than I did this morning, no better or worse, but every way the same. That redheaded little wretch! He'll rue the day if I ever find him again!"

---

jubilation: tremendous joy
crestfallen: feeling ashamed and humiliated
sheepish: embarrassed because of some mistake
rue: to regret

So saying, Maibon threw the stone into the fireplace. That night he grumbled his way to bed, dreaming revenge on the dishonest dwarf.

Next morning, after a restless night, he yawned, rubbed his eyes, and scratched his chin. Then he sat bolt upright in bed, patting his cheeks in amazement.

"My beard!" he cried, tumbling out and hurrying to tell his wife. "It hasn't grown! Not by a hair! Can it be the dwarf didn't cheat me after all?"

"Don't talk to me about beards," declared his wife as Maibon went to the fireplace, picked out the stone, and clutched it safely in both hands. "There's trouble enough in the chicken roost. Those eggs should have hatched by now, but the hen is still brooding on her nest."

"Let the chickens worry about that," answered Maibon. "Wife, don't you see what a grand thing's happened to me? I'm not a minute older than I was yesterday. Bless that generous-hearted dwarf!"

"Let me lay hands on him and I'll bless him," retorted Modrona. "That's all well and good for you. But what of me? You'll stay as you are, but I'll turn old and gray, and worn and wrinkled, and go doddering into my grave! And what of our little ones? They'll grow up and have children of their own. And grandchildren, and great-grandchildren. And you, younger than any of them. What a foolish sight you'll be!"

But Maibon, gleeful over his good luck, paid his wife no heed and only tucked the stone deeper into his pocket. Next day, however, the eggs had still not hatched.

"And the cow!" Modrona cried. "She's long past due to calve, and no sign of a young one ready to be born!"

"Don't bother me with cows and chickens," replied Maibon. "They'll all come right, in time. As for time, I've got all the time in the world!"

Having no appetite for breakfast, Maibon went out into his field. Of all the seeds he had sown there, however, he was surprised to see not one had sprouted. The field, which by now should have been covered with green shoots, lay bare and empty.

"Eh, things do seem a little late these days," Maibon said to himself. "Well, no hurry. It's that much less for me to do. The wheat isn't growing, but neither are the weeds."

Some days went by and still the eggs had not hatched, the cow had not calved, the wheat had not sprouted. And now Maibon saw that his apple tree showed no sign of even the smallest, greenest fruit.

"Maibon, it's the fault of that stone!" wailed his wife. "Get rid of the thing!"

"Nonsense," replied Maibon. "The season's slow, that's all."

Nevertheless, his wife kept at him and kept at him so much that Maibon at last, and very reluctantly, threw the stone out the cottage window. Not too far, though, for he had it in the back of his mind to go later and find it again.

Next morning he had no need to go looking for it, for there was the stone, sitting on the window ledge.

"You see?" said Maibon to his wife. "Here it is, back again. So it's a gift meant for me to keep."

"Maibon!" cried his wife. "Will you get rid of it! We've had nothing but trouble since you brought it into the house. Now the baby's fretting and fuming. Teething, poor little thing. But not a tooth to be seen! Maibon, that stone's bad luck and I want no part of it!"

Protesting it was none of his doing that the stone had come back, Maibon carried it into the vegetable patch. He dug a hole, not a very deep one, and put the stone into it.

Next day, there was the stone, above ground, winking and glittering.

"Maibon!" cried his wife. "Once and for all, if you care for your family, get rid of that cursed thing!"

Seeing no other way to keep peace in the household, Maibon regretfully and unwillingly took the stone and threw it down the well, where it splashed into the water and sank from sight.

But that night, while he was trying vainly to sleep, there came such a rattling and clattering that Maibon clapped his hands over his ears, jumped out of bed, and went stumbling into the yard. At the well the bucket was jiggling back and forth and up and down at the end of the rope, and in the bottom of the bucket was the stone.

Now Maibon began to be truly distressed, not only for the toothless baby, the calfless cow, the fruitless tree, and the hen sitting desperately on her eggs, but for himself as well.

"Nothing's moving along as it should," he groaned. "I can't tell one day from another. Nothing changes, there's nothing to look forward to, nothing to show for my work. Why sow if the seeds don't sprout? Why plant if there's never a harvest? Why eat if I don't get hungry? Why go to bed at night, or get up in the morning, or do anything at all? And the way it looks, so it will stay for ever and ever! I'll shrivel from boredom if nothing else!"

"Maibon," pleaded his wife, "for all our sakes, destroy the dreadful thing!"

Maibon tried now to pound the stone to dust with his heaviest mallet, but he could not so much as knock a chip from it. He put it against his grindstone without so much as scratching it. He set it on his anvil and belabored it with hammer and tongs, all to no avail.

At last he decided to bury the stone again, this time deeper than before. Picking up his shovel, he hurried to the field. But he suddenly halted and the shovel dropped from his hands. There, sitting cross-legged on a stump, was the dwarf.

"You!" shouted Maibon, shaking his fist. "Cheat! Villain! Trickster! I did you a good turn, and see how you've repaid it!"

The dwarf blinked at the furious Maibon. "You mortals are an ungrateful crew. I gave you what you wanted."

"You should have warned me!" burst out Maibon.

"I did," Doli snapped back. "You wouldn't listen. No, you yapped and yammered, bound to have your way. I told you we didn't like to give away those stones. When you mortals get hold of one, you stay just as you are—but so does everything around you. Before you know it, you're mired in time like a rock in the mud. You take my advice. Get rid of that stone as fast as you can."

"What do you think I've been trying to do?" blurted Maibon. "I've buried it, thrown it down the well, pounded it with a hammer—it keeps coming back to me!"

"That's because you really didn't want to give it up," Doli said. "In the back of your mind and the bottom of your heart, you didn't want to change along with the rest of the world. So long as you feel that way, the stone is yours."

"No, no!" cried Maibon. "I want no more of it. Whatever may happen, let it happen. That's better than nothing

---

mallet: a hammer-like tool

happening at all. I've had my share of being young; I'll take my share of being old. And when I come to the end of my days, at least I can say I've lived each one of them."

"If you mean that," answered Doli, "toss the stone onto the ground right there at the stump. Then get home and be about your business."

Maibon flung down the stone, spun around, and set off as fast as he could. When he dared at last to glance back over his shoulder, fearful the stone might be bouncing along at his heels, he saw no sign of it, or of the redheaded dwarf.

Maibon gave a joyful cry, for at that same instant the fallow field was covered with green blades of wheat, the branches of the apple tree bent to the ground, so laden they were with fruit. He ran to the cottage, threw his arms around his wife and children, and told them the good news. The hen hatched her chicks; the cow bore her calf. And Maibon laughed with glee when he saw the first tooth in the baby's mouth.

Never again did Maibon meet any of the Fair Folk, and he was just as glad of it. He and his wife and children and grandchildren lived many years, and Maibon was as proud of his white hair and long beard as he had been of his sturdy arms and legs.

"Stones are all right in their way," said Maibon. "But the trouble with them is, they don't grow."

---

fallow: inactive; plowed but with nothing growing
laden: weighed down; full

The Three Brass Pennies

a Chinese legend
retold by Augusta Huiell Seaman

It is in the good old-fashioned way that this fairy-story begins—as all such stories should—Once upon a time. And a very long time ago it was, in the faraway city of Wang Po, in that faraway country, China.

Within this city lived a young man, Ah Fo by name, who was poor in worldly goods, but of a rarely studious and thoughtful turn of mind.

One fine day it chanced that he was walking through the forest outside the city, thinking deeply on existence and the universe in general, when he came suddenly face to face with a huge spider web stretched across the path, in whose silky meshes a bee was wound and struggling vainly to be free, while an ugly spider sat in the center and watched its fruitless efforts.

Many might have dodged the web and sauntered on, leaving the hapless bee to its fate, but Ah Fo was not of this nature. He could not pass a helpless creature in trouble, if it was in his power to assist. Gingerly, therefore, he took an end of his cotton robe, extracted the bee from the web, and then, not daring to leave it near its enemy, so exhausted was it, he carried it to his home in the city.

---

fruitless: useless
sauntered: strolled
hapless: unlucky
gingerly: very carefully

There he placed it on his writing table to recover, while he himself sat down to resume his interrupted thoughts on philosophy. While he was so occupied, the bee slowly regained its strength, crawled to a cake of wet India ink, which the Chinese use for their writing instead of our liquid variety. There it remained standing for a moment, perfectly still. Then it lit on a sheet of blank paper. After that, it spread its wings and flew out of the window, quite unperceived by the dreaming Ah Fo.

It was when that young student awoke from his reverie, however, that a surprise awaited him. Looking about for the lately rescued bee, he could perceive no sign of him. But there before him, on a sheet of white paper, directly in the center where the bee had stood, was printed in fresh ink the Chinese character representing the word Gratitude!

It was an astonishing moment for Ah Fo. How the symbol had come there, he could not imagine; yet he could not but attribute it in some manner to the lately rescued insect. He spent the remainder of the day cogitating upon the question and lay awake half the night bewildered by the mystery. Early next morning, however, a solution arrived, for a note was sent to him, which read:

> *There is a reward awaiting you, Ah Fo, for mercy to a tiny creature in desperate plight, if you will call today at the fourth house on the Street of the Purple Lantern.*

---

lit: landed gently
unperceived: unnoticed
reverie: a daydream
cogitating: thinking intensely
bewildered: completely confused

Naturally, Ah Fo let no grass grow under his heels in seeking out the street and house designated. Here he found an old, old man, living in the utmost simplicity, who shook hands with himself within his voluminous sleeves (as is the Chinese custom of greeting) and bade Ah Fo to enter and be seated. When the young student had done so, the old man seated himself opposite and began:

"I know that you are bewildered by the affair which happened yesterday, but I will at once dispel the mystery. I am a magician. Through all these many years, I have devoted my power to the relief of suffering and the betterment of humanity. Long have I been pursued, however, by a fellow magician, more subtle than I and entirely unscrupulous, who would rid the city of me because I have been accustomed to undo much of his evil by my merciful arts.

"It has been well understood that, should he ever lure me into his clutches, my life would be forfeit, unless some kindly soul would rescue me. In that case, his power over me would vanish forever. Yesterday I changed myself into a bee, in order to fly quickly to some distant city where I was needed. He must have been spying upon me, for he changed himself into a huge spider, and in the forest, where I settled to rest awhile, he caught me in his wicked web. It was the first and only time this had ever happened, and I gave myself up for lost—when you appeared, and broke his spell over me forever.

"Now, I have little in worldly goods with which to reward you, but I have the power to make you rich and successful,

voluminous: full and billowing
dispel: to get rid of
subtle: crafty
unscrupulous: lacking morals
forfeit: lost

provided you use my gift properly and with discretion. Here are three brass pennies. They do not look any different from our ordinary money" (and indeed they did not, being simply the brass Chinese "cash" with a square hole in the middle of each), "but they are magic pennies, and he who possesses them may have a wish for each. This wish he may enjoy just so long as he keeps the penny in his possession, but he loses it, should he part with the coin. Only by mentioning these wishes to me, however, may they be attained."

Then the magician spread out the three pennies before him on the table and stared thoughtfully at Ah Fo through his great, square, horn-rimmed spectacles. "Let us now see," he began. "You will desire, no doubt, an unlimited supply of gold and jewels, a huge castle in the best part of the town, and the beautiful daughter of the emperor for your wife?"

He was about to touch the first penny with his forefinger, when Ah Fo raised his hand.

"A moment, I pray you!" began the student. "This is too serious a matter to be decided so speedily. I feel that the possessions you suggest might not be pure joy. Allow me, if you will, to go home and think this matter over. Tomorrow, after due consideration, I may be better able to come to a decision."

The magician smiled a benevolent and delighted smile. "I have not seen so much discretion and forethought in many a long day!" he exclaimed. "Go and consider the matter, by all means, and may Confucius guide your meditations!"

And Ah Fo took his departure.

---

discretion: care and judgement in decision-making
benevolent: kindhearted
forethought: thinking ahead
Confucius: an ancient Chinese philosopher known for his wisdom

The next morning he was early at the magician's house. "I have carefully considered the matter, O wise and generous one!" he announced.

"And what might your decision be?" asked the magician, as he spread out the three brass pennies before him.

"I would ask first," went on Ah Fo, "for the power to read accurately the thoughts of others; secondly, for the power to foretell my own future at least a month in advance of any given moment; third, for the power to acquire all learning without any effort!"

When he had finished, the magician sat back with a gasp, took off his spectacles and wiped them, put them on once more, and stared at Ah Fo in astonishment and not a little dismay. "This is most unusual," he stammered, "not to say somewhat dangerous! Have you duly considered, my son, the extent of all you ask?"

"I have duly considered," replied Ah Fo, "and I feel that nothing but these demands can satisfy me, if you intend to be so good as to grant any wishes. I have no others."

"Very well, then," agreed the magician, reluctantly, and he touched each penny before him, murmuring something in a language unknown to Ah Fo. Then he handed them to the young man, bidding him fasten each securely about his neck and touch the proper one of them when he made any of the three wishes. And he carefully indicated the wish represented by each penny, for they all bore slightly different markings.

"And now may I inquire what you intend to do?" asked the old man, curiously.

"I intend to go out and see all the world, acquire all wisdom and possibly, at the end, overthrow this dynasty and

dynasty: a line of rulers of the same family

become ruler of the Celestial Kingdom myself!" announced Ah Fo, grandly.

"You are perfectly equipped to do so. I wish you all success!" smiled the magician. But he gazed after the young man somewhat sadly as Ah Fo walked away. "Come back and see me, I beg, when you have attained your purpose!" he called after him.

When Ah Fo reached his home, elated by his rare fortune, he packed up his small belongings, in preparation for starting out on his tour of the world. He had decided that he would see his own country before going on to others, so he planned to cross the great river below the city and travel into the southern part of China.

But first, in order to test the power of his pennies, he touched the one enabling him to see into the future, in order that he might ascertain the wisdom of this plan. To his horror, he saw himself in a small boat, or sampan, on the river in the midst of a violent storm. The sampan was suddenly upset; he saw himself struggling in the waves and finally disappearing beneath the black water!

"This will never, never do!" he cried, trembling at a fate so terrible. "I was fortunate to have thought of looking the matter up before I started. Evidently the southern route is not safe. I will investigate the northern one, though I would have preferred the other." He consulted his penny, but only to behold himself traveling through the mountains, beset by bandits and left dying by the roadside.

Hurriedly he changed his plans again, with the thought of a western route across the country, this time to discover

---

elated: overjoyed
ascertain: to determine

himself lost in a burning desert, parched with thirst, stricken with a fever, and perishing alone under the pitiless sun. In a frenzy, he turned to the last resort, crying, "I will cross the seas out of this wretched country and see the rest of the world first!" But again his prophetic penny revealed to him a vision of himself captured by pirates and set to work at the galleys.

Pale with fright at the dangers he had so narrowly escaped, Ah Fo sat down to consider the matter.

"It is plain that fate does not intend me to carry out this part of my program at present," he meditated. "Perhaps it is because I am not sufficiently equipped. Possibly it might be a better plan to acquire all wisdom first, and I will then be better prepared to conquer this kingdom when the time comes. Study was ever a pleasure to me, and there are some knotty problems that have baffled me of late. With my newly acquired power, it will be quite delightful to wrestle with them!"

So he put his house in order once more, got out his books, and prepared for a tussle with a difficult mathematical problem. And as this was plainly the time to try out the qualities of another of his magic pennies, he touched the proper one hopefully. To his delighted astonishment, he read in his mind the working out of the problem and its answer as plainly as though they were written out in the book before him.

"Now this is truly wonderful!" he cried. "It has not taken me one moment to solve what I have been puzzling over for the past month. At this rate, I shall acquire all wisdom in a short week or so. Let us try another!"

---

stricken: suddenly overwhelmed
prophetic: predicting the future
galleys: ships moved mostly by slaves at the oars

He worked feverishly for a little less than an hour, at the end of which he found he had solved every problem in every branch of higher mathematics that had ever puzzled either him or any of the great mathematicians of the land. But, strangely enough, the delight and elation of the feat had somehow vanished.

"It is almost too easy!" he sighed. "It is like reading it out of a book, instead of achieving it after hours of painstaking and unsuccessful work. However, mathematics was never my favorite study. Let us try how it will work with other branches."

All that day he spent over his studies, with the assistance of the magic penny, discovering that the difficulties of each became as simple to him as the reading of a child's primer would seem to an old man. And more and more did the zest for the achievement of wisdom and learning, under these conditions, slip away from him. At length he closed his books with a dissatisfied exclamation.

"This power may prove to be very useful later," he mused, "but it has taken all the joy from study for me at the present time. Since the acquiring of wisdom is so easy, I need spend little time over it, I perceive. Perhaps it would be just as well, for my next move, to go about the city and visit my friends and try to find out just what they think of me, so I can judge whom I may count upon as supporters when the time comes for me to overthrow the dynasty and assume my place as monarch."

Forthwith he set out to visit his friend Tuan See, anxious to put to the test the powers of the last magic penny. He found his friend with his family, seated at the evening meal, and was cordially invited by Tuan See to join them at the

---

mused: thought deeply
cordially: in a polite and friendly way

repast. Ah Fo was about to comply with real pleasure, for he enjoyed a well-spread table and congenial company, when his fingers accidentally touched the third penny.

Plainly, as if it had been written on the wall before him, could he read the real, inner thoughts of Tuan See—thoughts which ran very much like this: "I hope that he has to go quickly! I hope that he cannot accept! There is so little of that dish of delicious bamboo-tips, I do not want to share it! And I am weary tonight. I do not wish to talk. He will probably stay till midnight, and I am ready to drop with sleep!"

It was as if Ah Fo had been struck a blow in the face. He could not have imagined such duplicity in the heretofore absolutely cordial and devoted friend. And yet, quick on its heels, came the memory that he had not infrequently felt the same way himself. This reading of other people's minds certainly had its inconveniences!

He hastily refused the invitation to dine, saying he had just dropped in to sit a few moments and must hurry on. Then, all the while fingering his third penny, he began to detail to his friend how easily he had solved that day some of the intricate problems they had often mused over unsuccessfully together. And he could not help but feel that Tuan See must be delighted and admire his success.

Tuan See certainly lavished upon him, in words, all the praise he had hoped for; yet the telltale penny kept revealing those horridly candid inner thoughts: "What a conceited coxcomb Ah Fo is getting to be! I always realized that he

congenial: friendly
duplicity: deceitfulness; being misleading
cordial: warm and sincerely friendly
intricate: complicated
lavished: heaped generously
conceited: full of oneself

could be tiresome, but he was never so much so as now. What do I care how many problems he has solved? I am only interested now in my work and my family. I wish he would go. I wish he would go! I wish he would go!"

Ah Fo rose and bade his friend a good-bye that was almost a sob. Out in the street, tears so blinded his eyes that he could scarcely see his way home. Once there, however, he shut his door and sat himself down to think it over, longing for guidance as he clutched the penny that was to show him all wisdom. Scene after scene flashed through his brain, detailing to him where he had felt precisely the same toward certain friends, Tuan See among them, when courtesy had demanded that he appear most cordial. Had they been able to read his heart, they would have discovered the same thoughts.

"After all, we are but human!" he mused. "Tuan See is no worse than I. But what am I to do now?" He spent the night in considering the question, and in the early morning sought once more the magician in the Street of the Purple Lantern.

"Kind old man," he said, "I beg you to take back these brass pennies. They have brought me nothing but woe, and I quite realize that it was all through my own silly choosing. I desire only to be as I was before!"

The old man looked at him with an understanding twinkle in his eye. "I rather thought it would be somewhat like this," he answered. "I felt that you were overreaching yourself in your desire for power. Better to have chosen the gold and jewels, the stately castle in the best part of town, and the beautiful daughter of our emperor. And, by the way, these can still be yours, if you care to have me change the power of the pennies!"

"No, no, no!" cried Ah Fo, wildly. "With all gratitude to you, I desire none of these things—less now than ever. If you would grant me three wishes, let them, I pray you, be these. Allow me to forget all that I have learned through the agency of these terrible pennies; give me a contented mind; and lastly, allow me to return to my studies with a new zest and the determination to rise by my own honest effort above all obstacles. It is all that I would ask!"

"It shall be as you say," smiled the magician, tapping him lightly on the forehead. "And for that you do not need the pennies. I can see that they would not have brought you happiness, in any case, since happiness lies within yourself. You had it before I ever met you, and lost it for a time in seeking after less desirable things. Farewell!"

Ah Fo went out into the street, a contented and happy man once more. And the magician, after thoughtfully considering the brass pennies for a time, took them in his hand, walked out to the bank of the river, and hurled them far into its deep, engulfing tide.

agency: power
zest: enthusiasm
obstacles: barriers

THE MAGIC PRISON

by Elizabeth Harrison

PART 1

Little Harweda was born a prince. His father was king over a great land, and his mother was the most beautiful queen the world had ever seen. Prince Harweda was their only child. From the day of his birth, everything that love or money could do for him had been done.

But his parents never thought of making the young prince care for anything but himself. He had never in all his life given up one of his comforts that somebody else might have a pleasure. So, of course, he grew to be selfish; and by the time he was five years old he was so very disagreeable that nobody loved him.

"Dear, dear! What shall we do?" said the poor queen mother, and the king only sighed and answered, "Ah, what indeed!"

They were both very much grieved at heart, for they well knew that little Harweda, although he was a prince, would never grow up to be a really great king unless he could make his people love him.

At last they decided to send for his fairy godmother to see if she could find a way to cure Prince Harweda of thinking of nothing but himself.

"Well, well, well!" exclaimed the godmother, when they had laid the case before her. "This is a pretty state of affairs! And I his godmother, too! Why wasn't I called in sooner?"

---

state of affairs: a situation

She told them that she would have to think a day and a night and another day before she could offer them any help. "But," she added, "if I take the child in charge, you must promise not to meddle for a whole year."

The king and queen gladly promised that they would not speak to their son, or even see him during that time, if the fairy godmother would only cure him of his selfishness.

"We'll see about that," said the godmother. "Humph! Expecting to be a king some day and not caring for anybody but himself—a fine king he'll make!" With that, off she flew; and the king and queen saw nothing more of her for a day and a night and another day. Then back she came in a great hurry.

"Give me the prince," said she. "I have his house all ready for him. One month from today I'll bring him back to you. Perhaps he'll be cured, and perhaps he won't. If he is not cured, then we shall try two months next time. We'll see."

Without more ado, she picked up the astonished young prince and flew away with him as lightly as if he were nothing but a feather or a straw.

They flew a long distance until they reached a great forest. When they had come to the middle of it, down flew the fairy. In a minute more the young prince was standing on the green grass beside a beautiful pink-marble palace that looked somewhat like a good-sized summerhouse.

"This is your home," said the godmother. "In it you will find everything you need, and you can do just as you choose with your time."

---

meddle: to interfere

Little Harweda was delighted at this, for there was nothing in the world he liked better than to do as he pleased. He tossed his cap up into the air and ran into the lovely little house without so much as saying "Thank you" to his godmother.

"Humph!" she said, as he disappeared. "You'll have enough of it before you are through, my fine prince." And away she flew.

PART 2

Prince Harweda had no sooner set his foot inside the small rose-colored palace than the iron door shut with a bang and locked itself. For you must know by this time that it was an enchanted house, as, of course, all houses are that are built by fairies.

His fairy godmother had told him that it was his house; therefore he was interested in looking at everything in it. From the middle of the ceiling hung a large gilded bird cage containing a beautiful bird, which just at this moment was singing a glad song of welcome to the prince. Harweda, however, cared very little about birds, so he took no notice of the songster.

Wonderfully carved jars and vases of gold and silver stood about the floor, and each was filled with a different kind of perfume.

"This is delicious," said Prince Harweda. "Now I can have all the sweet odors I want without the trouble of going out into the garden for flowers."

In the center of the room was a fountain of sparkling water, which leaped up and fell back into its marble basin with a faint, dreamy music very pleasant to hear.

---

gilded: covered with a thin layer of gold

On a table near at hand stood baskets of the most tempting pears and grapes and peaches, and near them were dishes of all kinds of sweetmeats.

"Good!" cried the greedy young prince. "That is what I like best of all." And he fell to eating the fruit and sweetmeats as fast as he could cram them into his mouth.

But, strange to say, no sooner did he reach his hand out for a soft, mellow pear or a rich, juicy peach than another pear or peach took its place.

After Prince Harweda had eaten until he could eat no more, he threw himself down on one of the couches and soon fell asleep. When he awoke he noticed for the first time the walls, which, by the way, were really the strangest part of his new home. They had in them twelve long, checkered windows which reached from the ceiling to the floor. The spaces between the windows were filled with mirrors exactly the same size as the windows, so that the whole room was walled in with windows and mirrors.

PART 3

But little Prince Harweda scarcely glanced out of the windows at all, he was so taken up with the broad, handsome mirrors; for in each of them he could see himself, and he was very fond of gazing at his reflection. He was much pleased when he noticed that the mirrors were so arranged that he could see himself in several of them at the same time. He could thus see his front and back and each side all together. As he was a handsome boy, he enjoyed these many views of himself immensely.

---

sweetmeats: candy
immensely: very much

He spent so much time gazing into the wonderful mirrors that he had very little use for the books and games that had been placed there for him. He spent hours each day before first one mirror and then another; and he did not notice that the windows were growing narrower and the mirrors wider. In fact, the windows had become so small that they hardly admitted light enough for him to see himself in the mirrors.

Still, this did not alarm him very much, as he cared nothing whatever for the outside world. The windows at last became mere slits in the wall, and the mirrors grew so large that they reflected not only little Harweda, but all the room besides in a dim kind of way.

Finally, however, Prince Harweda awoke one morning and found himself in total darkness. Not a ray of light came from the outside; and, of course, not an object in the room could be seen. He rubbed his eyes and sat up to make sure that he was not dreaming. Then he called loudly for someone to open a window for him, but no one came.

He got up and felt his way to the iron door and tried to open it; but, as you know, it was locked. He kicked it and beat upon it, but he only bruised his fists and hurt his toes. He grew quite angry now. How dare anyone shut him, a prince, in a dark prison like this! He cried out against his fairy godmother, calling her all sorts of horrid names. Then he blamed his father and mother; in fact, he blamed everybody and everything but himself.

But it was of no use. The sound of his own voice was his only answer. The whole of the outside world seemed to have forgotten him.

As he felt his way back to his couch he knocked over one of the golden jars that had held the liquid perfume; the odor

admitted: let in

was all gone now, and only an empty jar rolled over the floor. He laid himself down on the couch, but its soft pillows had been removed, and an iron framework received him.

He was dismayed, and lay for a long time trying to think what he had best do with himself. All before him was blank darkness, as black as the darkest night you ever saw. He reached out his hand to get some fruit to eat, but only one or two withered apples remained on the table. Was he to starve to death?

Suddenly he noticed that the tinkling music of the fountain had ceased. He hastily felt his way over to it, and he found in place of the dancing, running stream a silent pool of water. A hush had fallen upon everything about him; a dead silence was in the room. He threw himself down upon the floor and wished that he were dead, too.

At last he heard, or thought he heard, a faint sound. He listened eagerly. It seemed to be some tiny creature not far from him trying to move about. For the first time for nearly a month, he remembered the bird in its gilded cage.

"Poor little thing!" he cried, as he sprang up; "you too are shut within this terrible prison. This thick darkness must be as hard for you to bear as it is for me."

He went toward the cage, and as he came near, the bird gave a sad little chirp.

"You must need some water to drink, poor thing!" he said, filling its drinking cup. "This is all I have to give you."

Just then he heard a harsh, grating sound, as of rusty bolts sliding with difficulty out of their sockets; and then faint rays of light, not wider than a hair, began to shine between the heavy mirrors. Prince Harweda was filled with joy.

---

dismayed: disappointed; discouraged
withered: dried out

"Perhaps, perhaps," said he, softly, "I may yet see the light again. Ah, how beautiful the outside world would look to me now!"

The next day he was so hungry that he began to eat one of the old withered apples, and as he bit it he thought of the bird, his fellow prisoner.

"You must be hungry, too, poor little thing!" he said, putting part of his apple into the bird's cage.

Again came the harsh, grating sound, and the boy noticed that the cracks of light were growing larger. Still, they were only cracks; nothing of the outside world could be seen. But it was a comfort not to have to feel his way about in total darkness. Prince Harweda went up to one of the cracks and, putting his eye close to it, as he would to a pinhole in a paper, was glad to find that he could tell the greenness of the grass from the blue of the sky.

Then he climbed up into a chair and unfastened the bird cage from the golden chain by which it hung. He carried it carefully to the nearest crack of light and placed it close to the narrow opening. Once more he heard the harsh, grating sound, and the wall moved a bit; the windows were now at least an inch wide.

At this the poor prince clasped his hands with delight. He sat down near the bird cage and gazed out of the narrow opening. Never before had the trees looked so tall and stately, or the white clouds floating through the sky so lovely.

The next day, as he was carefully cleaning the bird's cage, the walls again creaked and groaned, and the mirrors grew narrower as the windows widened. But Prince Harweda saw only the flood of sunshine that poured in and the beauty of

stately: grand

the larger landscape. He cared nothing whatever now for the stupid mirrors, which could only reflect what was placed before them.

One day, as two white doves suddenly soared aloft in the blue sky, the poor little bird, who had now become the prince's comrade, gave a pitiful little trill.

"Dear little fellow," cried Prince Harweda, "do you also long for your freedom? You shall at least be as free as I am." So saying, he opened the cage door and the bird flew out.

One day, soon after this, the little bird fluttered up against the windowpane and beat his wings against it in a vain effort to get out. A new idea seized the young prince. He took up a golden jar, went to the window, and struck on one of its checkered panes of glass with all his force.

"You shall be free, even if I cannot be," he said to the bird. Two or three strong blows shivered the small pane, and the bird swept out into the free air beyond.

"Ah, my pretty one, how glad I am that you are free at last!" cried the prince, watching the flight of his fellow prisoner. His face was bright with glad, unselfish joy.

The small pink-marble palace shook from top to bottom, the iron door flew open, and the fresh wind from the sea rushed in. Prince Harweda could hardly believe his eyes as he sprang to the door. There stood his fairy godmother, smiling, with her hand stretched out toward him.

"Come, my godchild," she said gently, "we will now go back to your father and mother, the king and queen."

Great indeed was the rejoicing in the palace when Prince Harweda was returned to them a changed boy, kind and

---

comrade: a friend
trill: a musical sound
vain: useless

thoughtful to all about him. Many a struggle he had with himself and his old habit of selfishness; but as time passed by he grew to be a great and wise king, tenderly caring for all his people, and loved by them in return.

KADDO'S WALL

a West African folktale
as told by Harold Courlander and George Herzog

In the town of Tendella in the Kingdom of Seno, north of the Gulf of Guinea, there was a rich man by the name of Kaddo. His fields spread out on every side of the town. At plowing time hundreds of men and boys hoed up his fields, and then hundreds of women and girls planted his corn seed in the ground for him. His grain bulged in his granary, because each season he harvested far more than he could use. The name of Kaddo was known far and wide throughout the Kingdom of Seno. Travelers who passed through the town carried tales of his wealth far beyond Seno's borders.

One day Kaddo called all of his people in the town of Tendella together for a big meeting in front of his house. They all came, for Kaddo was an important man, and they knew he was going to make an important announcement.

"There's something that bothers me," Kaddo said. "I've been thinking about it for a long time. I've lain awake worrying. I have so much corn in my granary that I don't know what to do with it."

The people listened attentively, and thought about Kaddo's words. Then a man said: "Some of the people of the town have no corn at all. They are very poor and have nothing. Why don't you give some of your corn to them?"

Kaddo shook his head and said, "No, that isn't a very good idea. It doesn't satisfy me."

---

granary: a building used to store grain

Another man said to Kaddo, "Well, then, you could lend corn to the people who have had a bad harvest and have no seed for the spring planting. That would be very good for the town and would keep poverty away."

"No," Kaddo said, "that's no solution either."

"Well, then, why not sell some of your corn and buy cattle instead?" still another man said.

Kaddo shook his head.

"No, it's not very good advice. It's hard for people to advise a rich man with problems like mine."

Many people made suggestions, but nobody's advice suited Kaddo. He thought for a while, and at last he said, "Send me as many young girls as you can find. I will have them grind the corn for me."

The people went away. They were angry with Kaddo. But the next day they sent a hundred girls to work for him as he had asked. On a hundred grindstones they began to grind Kaddo's corn into flour. All day long they put corn into the grindstones and took flour out. All day long the people of the town heard the sound of the grinding at Kaddo's house. A pile of corn flour began to grow. For seven days and seven nights the girls ground corn without a pause.

When the last grain of corn was ground into flour, Kaddo called the girls together and said, "Now bring water from the spring. We shall mix it with the corn flour to make mortar out of it."

So the girls brought water in water pots and mixed it with the flour to make a thick mortar. Then Kaddo ordered them to make bricks out of the mortar.

"When the bricks are dry, then I shall make a wall of them around my house," he said.

mortar: a mixture used to hold bricks or stones together

Word went out that Kaddo was preparing to build a wall of flour around his house, and the people of the town came to his door and protested.

"You can't do a thing like this; it is against humanity!" they said.

"It's not right, people have no right to build walls with food!" a man said.

"Ah, what is right and what is wrong?" Kaddo said. "My right is different from yours, because I am so very rich. So leave me alone."

"Corn is to eat, so that you may keep alive," another said. "It's not meant to taunt those who are less fortunate."

"When people are hungry it is an affront to shut them out with a wall of flour," another man said.

"Stop your complaints," Kaddo said. "The corn is mine. It is my surplus. I can't eat it all. It comes from my own fields. I am rich. What good is it to be rich if you can't do what you want with your own property?"

The people of the town went away, shaking their heads in anger over Kaddo's madness. The hundred girls continued to make bricks of flour, which they dried in the sun. And when the bricks were dry Kaddo had them begin building the wall around his house. They used wet dough for mortar to hold the bricks together, and slowly the wall grew. They stuck cowry shells into the wall to make beautiful designs, and when at last the wall was done, and the last corn flour used up, Kaddo was very proud. He walked back and forth and looked at his wall. He walked around it. He went in and out of the gate. He was very happy.

---

taunt: to mock
surplus: an amount more than is needed; an excess
cowry shells: brightly colored shells

And now when people came to see him they had to stand by the gate until he asked them to enter. When the workers who plowed and planted for Kaddo wanted to talk to him, Kaddo sat on the wall by the gate and listened to them and gave them orders. And whenever the people of the town wanted his opinion on an important matter he sat on his wall and gave it to them, while they stood and listened.

Things went on like this for a long time. Kaddo enjoyed his reputation as the richest man for miles around. The story of Kaddo's wall went to the farthest parts of the kingdom.

And then one year there was a bad harvest for Kaddo. There wasn't enough rain to grow the corn, and the earth dried up hard and dusty like the road. There wasn't a single ear of corn in all of Kaddo's fields or the fields of his relatives.

The next year it was the same. Kaddo had no seed corn left, so he sold his cattle and horses to buy corn for food and seed for a new planting. He sowed corn again, but the next harvest time it was the same, and there wasn't a single ear of corn in all his fields.

Year after year Kaddo's crops failed. Some of his relatives died of hunger, and others went away to other parts of the Kingdom of Seno, for they had no more seed corn to plant and they couldn't count on Kaddo's help. Kaddo's workers ran away, because he was unable to feed them. Gradually Kaddo's part of the town became deserted. All that he had left were a young daughter and a mangy donkey.

When his cattle and his money were all gone, Kaddo became very hungry. He scraped away a little bit of the flour wall and ate it. The next day he scraped away more of the flour wall and ate it. The wall got lower and lower. Little by

---

mangy: affected by a skin disease that usually causes loss of hair

little it disappeared. A day came when the wall was gone, when nothing was left of the elegant structure Kaddo had built around his house, and on which he had used to sit to listen to the people of the town when they came to ask him to lend them a little seed corn.

Then Kaddo realized that if he was to live any longer he must get help from somewhere. He wondered who would help him. Not the people of Tendella, for he had insulted and mistreated them, and they would have nothing to do with him. There was only one man he could go to, Sogole, king of the Ganna people, who had the reputation of being very rich and generous.

So Kaddo and his daughter got on the mangy, underfed donkey and rode seven days until they arrived in the land of the Ganna.

Sogole sat before his royal house when Kaddo arrived. He had a soft skin put on the ground next to him for Kaddo to sit upon, and had millet brew brought for the two of them to drink.

"Well, stranger in the land of the Ganna, take a long drink, for you have a long trip behind you if you come from Tendella," Sogole said.

"Thank you, but I can't drink much," Kaddo said.

"Why is that?" Sogole said. "When people are thirsty they drink."

"That is true," Kaddo replied. "But I have been hungry too long, and my stomach is shrunk."

"Well, drink in peace then, because now that you are my guest you won't be hungry. You shall have whatever you need from me."

---

millet: a kind of grain

Kaddo nodded his head solemnly and drank a little of the millet brew.

"And now tell me," Sogole said. "You say you come from the town of Tendella in the Kingdom of Seno? I've heard many tales of that town. The famine came there and drove out many people, because they had no corn left."

"Yes," Kaddo said. "Hard times drove them out, and the corn was all gone."

"But tell me, there was a rich and powerful man in Tendella named Kaddo, wasn't there? What ever happened to him? Is he still alive?"

"Yes, he is still alive," Kaddo said.

"A fabulous man, this Kaddo," Sogole said. "They say he built a wall of flour around his house out of his surplus crops, and when he talked to his people he sat on the wall by his gate. Is this true?"

"Yes, it is true," Kaddo said sadly.

"Does he still have as many cattle as he used to?" Sogole asked.

"No, they are all gone."

"It is an unhappy thing for a man who owned so much to come to so little," Sogole said. "But doesn't he have many servants and workers still?"

"His workers and servants are all gone," Kaddo said. "Of all his great household he has only one daughter left. The rest went away because there was no money and no food."

Sogole looked melancholy. "Ah, what is a rich man when his cattle are gone and his servants have left him? But tell me, what happened to the wall of flour that he built around his house?"

---

melancholy: sad; gloomy

"He ate the wall," Kaddo said. "Each day he scraped a little of the flour from the wall, until it was all gone."

"A strange story," Sogole said. "But such is life."

And he thought quietly for a while about the way life goes for people sometimes, and then he asked: "And were you, by any chance, one of Kaddo's family?"

"Indeed I was one of Kaddo's family. Once I was rich. Once I had more cattle than I could count. Once I had many cornfields. Once I had hundreds of workers cultivating my crops. Once I had a bursting granary. Once I was Kaddo, the great personage of Tendella."

"What! You yourself are Kaddo?"

"Yes, once I was proud and lordly, and now I sit in rags begging for help."

"What can I do for you?" Sogole asked.

"I have nothing left now. Give me some seed corn, so that I can go back and plant my fields again."

"Take what you need," Sogole said. He ordered his servants to bring bags of corn and to load them on Kaddo's donkey. Kaddo thanked him humbly, and he and his daughter started their return trip to Tendella.

They traveled for seven days. On the way Kaddo became very hungry. He hadn't seen so much corn for a long time as he was bringing back from the Kingdom of the Ganna. He took a few grains and put them in his mouth and chewed them. Once more he put a few grains in his mouth. Then he put a whole handful in his mouth and swallowed. He couldn't stop. He ate and ate. He forgot that this was the corn with which he had to plant his fields. When he arrived in Tendella he went to his bed to sleep, and when he arose

---

personage: a notable person

the next morning he ate again. He ate so much of the corn that he became sick. He went to his bed again and cried out in pain, because his stomach had forgotten what to do with food. And before long Kaddo died.

Kaddo's grandchildren and great-grandchildren in the Kingdom of Seno are poor to this day. And to the rich men of the country the common people sometimes say:

"Don't build a wall of flour around your house."

THE STORY OF BABA ABDALLA
an Arabian Nights tale

Once upon a time, the caliph Haroun al Raschid and his grand vizier, disguised as merchants, were proceeding across a bridge in the city of Baghdad. Along their way, they met a blind man begging for alms. The caliph gave him a piece of gold and was much surprised at the old man's response. "Pray, sir," said the old man, "give me a box on the ear. Otherwise I shall be unable to accept your alms, without breaking a solemn vow."

After some hesitation, the caliph obeyed this strange request, and gave the old man a very slight blow, and then continued on his walk. When they had gone a little way, the caliph said to the vizier, "Return and tell that blind man to come to my palace tomorrow at the hour of afternoon prayer, for I would hear his history, which must be strange." The vizier hastened to obey, and then resumed his walk with the caliph.

The next day the blind man appeared at the palace, where he was introduced into the caliph's presence by the grand vizier. He prostrated himself before the throne, and when he rose up, the caliph asked him his name. The blind man answered that it was Baba Abdalla.

caliph: a Muslim leader
vizier: a high-ranking Muslim official
alms: charity
hastened: moved quickly
prostrated: bowed face down

"Baba Abdalla," said the caliph, "tell me why you require those who give you alms to give you also a box on the ear."

The blind man, having bowed low, replied, "Sir, I will tell you; and you will see that this action is but a slight penance for a great crime of which I am guilty." Then he went on to tell this story:

I was born in Baghdad, and at an early age found myself in possession of considerable wealth. Soon I began to trade with all the cities of the land.

One of my journeys led me to Bussorah. When I was returning with my unladen camels, I met a dervish, with whom I sat down to eat.

During our meal, the dervish told me that he knew of a spot close by where there were such immense riches that, if all my fourscore camels were loaded with gold and jewels from it, nothing would be missed there.

I was delighted by what I heard, and begged the dervish to conduct me to the spot. Whereupon he replied, "I am ready to conduct you to the place where the treasure lies. We will load your fourscore camels with jewels and gold, but only if, once they are loaded, you will let me have one half, and you will be content with the other half. After that we will separate and take our camels where we may think fit. You see this is an entirely fair division, for if you give me forty camels, you will procure, by my help, enough to purchase thousands."

---

penance: voluntary self-punishment to make up for some wrongdoing
unladen: not weighed down
dervish: a member of a Muslim religious order
fourscore: eighty (one score is twenty)
procure: to get; to obtain

Although avarice made me unwilling to give up so much, I had no choice but to accept the terms the dervish offered. As soon as he had heard my decision, he led me to the place.

It was a valley situated between two high mountains, so secluded that there was no fear of discovery. When we arrived there, the dervish quickly collected some sticks and kindled a fire. As he muttered mysterious words, a dense smoke arose from the fire. When this had cleared away, I saw that the sides of the cliff had rolled back. A magnificent palace was revealed in the side of the mountain, with great heaps of treasure lying about.

Like a greedy bird of prey, I seized the gold and filled my sacks, until I saw that the dervish paid more heed to the jewels. I followed his example, so that we took away more jewels than gold. Among other things, the dervish took a small golden vase that contained nothing more than a sticky ointment. And after we had loaded our camels, he closed the rock by using some mystic words.

J.Rae

avarice: greed
mystic: magical

49

We now divided the camels, each taking forty. We traveled together till we came to the great road where we were to part, the dervish to go to Bussorah, and I to Baghdad. We embraced each other with great joy, and started on our different routes.

I had not gone far before the demon of ingratitude and envy took possession of my heart. I mourned the loss of my camels, but even more the riches with which they were loaded. "The dervish," said I to myself, "has no need for all this wealth, since he is master of the treasure and may have as much as he pleases." So I gave myself up to the coldest ingratitude, and determined immediately to take from him the camels with their load.

To carry out this plan, I called to him as loudly as I could, pretending I had something important to say, and made a sign to him to stop, which he did.

When I came up to him, I said, "Brother, I had no sooner parted from you than a thought came into my head. You are used to living apart from the world, intent only upon serving God. You know not, perhaps, what trouble you have taken upon yourself, to take care of so many camels. Hear my advice and keep but thirty. You will find that number hard enough to manage. Take my word; I have had experience."

The dervish, who seemed rather afraid of me, at once had me choose ten camels from his forty. This I promptly did, and joined them with my forty.

The readiness with which he had given up these ten only increased my desire for more. "Brother," said I, "thirty camels are too many for you to manage, since you are not used to the work. Therefore I beg you relieve yourself of ten more."

My request was promptly granted by the dervish, who gave me ten more camels. He now had but twenty left, and I was master of sixty, and might boast of greater riches than any sovereign prince. Anyone would have thought I should now be content, but I only became greedier and more desirous of the other twenty camels.

I pleaded even more strongly in order to make the dervish grant me ten of his remaining twenty camels, which he did with good grace. And as to the ten he had left, I embraced him, kissed his feet, and begged him not to refuse me. And at length he crowned my joy by giving me them also.

Then into my head came the thought that the little vase the dervish had shown me probably contained something more precious than all the riches I had. I longed to possess it, so I said, "What will you do with that little vase of ointment? It seems such a trifle, it is not worth carrying away. Will you not make me a present of it? What use has a dervish, who has renounced the vanities of the world, for perfumes or scented ointments?"

Would to heaven he had refused me that vase! But if he had, I was stronger than he, and would have taken it from him by force.

The dervish readily pulled it out of his robe, and presented it to me with the best grace in the world, saying, "Here, take it, brother, and be content. If I can do more for you, you need but to ask me."

When I had the vase in my hand, I opened it, and said to him, "Since you are so good, I am sure you will not refuse the favor of telling me the special use of this ointment."

"The use is very surprising and wonderful," replied the dervish. "By applying a little of it around the left eye, you

---

sovereign: having absolute power
trifle: a small, unimportant thing
renounced: given up
vanities: worthless, useless things

can at once see all the treasures contained in the earth. But if you apply it to the right eye, you will become blind."

At my request, the dervish applied the ointment to my left eye, and I found that he had indeed spoken truly. I saw vast riches and longed to grasp them all. I then bade him put some around my right eye.

"Pray remember," said the dervish, "that you will immediately become blind."

Far from being persuaded that the dervish was telling the truth, I imagined that he was trying to hide some mystery from me.

"Brother," replied I, smiling, "I see plainly you wish to mislead me. It is not natural that this ointment should have two such contrary effects."

"The matter is as I tell you," replied the dervish. "You ought to believe me, for I cannot conceal the truth."

I would not believe the dervish, although he spoke like an honest man. My great desire to possess all the treasures in the world had such an effect on me that I would not heed his warnings. I could not believe his words, which were, however, all too true, as I soon found out.

Since the ointment, by being applied to the left eye, had the power to show me all the treasures of the earth, I was sure that, by being applied to the right, it might have the power of giving the treasures into my hand. Possessed with this thought, I urged the dervish to apply the ointment to my right eye.

"Brother," said he, "after I have done you so much service, I cannot do you so great an injury. Consider what a misfortune it is to be deprived of one's eyesight. Do not force me to do a thing which you will be sorry for all your life."

---

bade: commanded

I persisted, however, and said in strong terms, "Brother, lay aside all your objections. You have granted me all that I have asked of you hitherto. Would you have me go away dissatisfied about a thing of so little consequence? Grant me, I pray you, this last favor. Whatever happens, I will not lay the blame on you, but take it upon myself alone."

The dervish, having made all the resistance possible, finally took a little of the fatal ointment and applied it to my right eye. Then, alas, I immediately became blind, as you see me now.

"Ah! dervish," I exclaimed in agony, "what you warned me of has proved too true. Fatal curiosity," added I, "foolish desire of riches, into what depths of misery have they cast me! But you, dear brother, who are so charitable and good, among your wonderful secrets, have you not one that will restore to me my sight?"

"Miserable wretch!" answered the dervish, "if you had only heeded my advice, you would have avoided this misfortune, but you now have what you deserve. The blindness of your mind was the cause of the loss of your eyes. Pray to God, therefore, to restore your eyesight. He gave you riches, of which you were unworthy. On that account, he takes them from you again, and by my hands will give them to men not so ungrateful as you are."

The dervish left me to myself, overcome with despair. After he had collected my camels, he drove them away and continued on the road to Bussorah.

Thus deprived of sight and all I had in the world, I should have died with affliction and hunger, if the next day a caravan had not received me charitably and brought me back to Baghdad.

---

hitherto: before; previously
caravan: a group of people traveling together

And so was I reduced to beggary. As a punishment for my offense, I now ask every person who gives me alms to give me also a box on the ear.

This is the explanation of what seemed so strange to your Majesty yesterday. I ask your pardon once more, and submit to whatever punishment I deserve.

"Baba Abdalla," replied the caliph, "you may cease to beg publicly, and to show my appreciation of your remorse and my approval of the punishment you have inflicted on yourself, I order my grand vizier to pay you daily hereafter four pieces of silver money."

At these words, Baba Abdalla prostrated himself before the caliph's throne, returned him thanks, and wished him all happiness and prosperity.

---

remorse: feelings of guilt and regret for the wrongs one has done

ANIMALS AND THEIR PEOPLE

Zlateh the Goat

by Isaac Bashevis Singer
translated by the author and Elizabeth Shub

At Hanukkah time the road from the village to the town is usually covered with snow, but this year the winter had been a mild one. Hanukkah had almost come, yet little snow had fallen. The sun shone most of the time. The peasants complained that because of the dry weather there would be a poor harvest of winter grain. New grass sprouted, and the peasants sent their cattle out to pasture.

For Reuven the furrier it was a bad year, and after long hesitation he decided to sell Zlateh the goat. She was old and gave little milk. Feivel the town butcher had offered eight gulden for her. Such a sum would buy Hanukkah candles, potatoes and oil for pancakes, gifts for the children, and other holiday necessaries for the house. Reuven told his oldest boy Aaron to take the goat to town.

Aaron understood what taking the goat to Feivel meant, but had to obey his father. Leah, his mother, wiped the tears from her eyes when she heard the news. Aaron's younger sisters, Anna and Miriam, cried loudly. Aaron put on his quilted jacket and a cap with earmuffs, bound a rope around Zlateh's neck, and took along two slices of bread with cheese to eat on the road. Aaron was supposed to deliver the goat by evening, spend the night at the butcher's, and return the next day with the money.

---

furrier: one who makes or repairs fur garments
gulden: a kind of money

While the family said goodbye to the goat, and Aaron placed the rope around her neck, Zlateh stood as patiently and good-naturedly as ever. She licked Reuven's hand. She shook her small white beard. Zlateh trusted human beings. She knew that they always fed her and never did her any harm.

When Aaron brought her out on the road to town, she seemed somewhat astonished. She'd never been led in that direction before. She looked back at him questioningly, as if to say, "Where are you taking me?" But after a while she seemed to come to the conclusion that a goat shouldn't ask questions. Still, the road was different. They passed new fields, pastures, and huts with thatched roofs. Here and there a dog barked and came running after them, but Aaron chased it away with his stick.

The sun was shining when Aaron left the village. Suddenly the weather changed. A large black cloud with a bluish center appeared in the east and spread itself rapidly over the sky. A cold wind blew in with it. The crows flew low, croaking. At first it looked as if it would rain, but instead it began to hail as in summer. It was early in the day, but it became dark as dusk. After a while the hail turned to snow.

In his twelve years Aaron had seen all kinds of weather, but he had never experienced a snow like this one. It was so dense it shut out the light of the day. In a short time their path was completely covered. The wind became as cold as ice. The road to town was narrow and winding. Aaron no longer knew where he was. He could not see through the snow. The cold soon penetrated his quilted jacket.

At first Zlateh didn't seem to mind the change in weather. She, too, was twelve years old and knew what winter meant.

But when her legs sank deeper and deeper into the snow, she began to turn her head and look at Aaron in wonderment. Her mild eyes seemed to ask, "Why are we out in such a storm?" Aaron hoped that a peasant would come along with his cart, but no one passed by.

The snow grew thicker, falling to the ground in large, whirling flakes. Beneath it Aaron's boots touched the softness of a plowed field. He realized that he was no longer on the road. He had gone astray. He could no longer figure out which was east or west, which way was the village, the town. The wind whistled, howled, whirled the snow about in eddies. It looked as if white imps were playing tag on the fields. A white dust rose above the ground. Zlateh stopped. She could walk no longer. Stubbornly she anchored her cleft hooves in the earth and bleated as if pleading to be taken home. Icicles hung from her white beard, and her horns were glazed with frost.

Aaron did not want to admit the danger, but he knew just the same that if they did not find shelter they would freeze to death. This was no ordinary storm. It was a mighty blizzard. The snowfall had reached his knees. His hands were numb, and he could no longer feel his toes. He choked when he breathed. His nose felt like wood, and he rubbed it with snow. Zlateh's bleating began to sound like crying. Those humans in whom she had so much confidence had dragged her into a trap. Aaron began to pray to God for himself and for the innocent animal.

Suddenly he made out the shape of a hill. He wondered what it could be. Who had piled snow into such a huge

wonderment: amazement
eddies: circular currents
cleft: partially split

heap? He moved toward it, dragging Zlateh after him. When he came near it, he realized that it was a large haystack which the snow had blanketed.

Aaron realized immediately that they were saved. With great effort he dug his way through the snow. He was a village boy and knew what to do. When he reached the hay, he hollowed out a nest for himself and the goat. No matter how cold it may be outside, in the hay it is always warm. And hay was food for Zlateh. The moment she smelled it she became contented and began to eat. Outside, the snow continued to fall. It quickly covered the passageway Aaron had dug. But a boy and an animal need to breathe, and there was hardly any air in their hideout. Aaron bored a kind of a window through the hay and snow and carefully kept the passage clear.

Zlateh, having eaten her fill, sat down on her hind legs and seemed to have regained her confidence in man. Aaron ate his two slices of bread and cheese, but after the difficult journey he was still hungry. He looked at Zlateh and noticed her udders were full. He lay down next to her, placing himself so that when he milked her he could squirt the milk into his mouth. It was rich and sweet. Zlateh was not accustomed to being milked that way, but she did not resist. On the contrary, she seemed eager to reward Aaron for bringing her to a shelter whose very walls, floor, and ceiling were made of food.

Through the window Aaron could catch a glimpse of the chaos outside. The wind carried before it whole drifts of snow. It was completely dark, and he did not know whether night had already come or whether it was the darkness of the storm. Thank God that in the hay it was not cold. The dried hay, grass, and field flowers exuded the warmth of the summer sun. Zlateh ate frequently; she nibbled from above, below, from the left and right. Her body gave forth an animal warmth, and Aaron cuddled up to her. He had always loved Zlateh, but now she was like a sister. He was alone, cut off from his family, and wanted to talk. He began to talk to Zlateh. "Zlateh, what do you think about what has happened to us?" he asked.

"Maaaa," Zlateh answered.

"If we hadn't found this stack of hay, we would both be frozen stiff by now," Aaron said.

"Maaaa," was the goat's reply.

"If the snow keeps on falling like this, we may have to stay here for days," Aaron explained.

"Maaaa," Zlateh bleated.

"What does 'maaaa' mean?" Aaron asked. "You'd better speak up clearly."

"Maaaa, maaaa," Zlateh tried.

"Well, let it be 'maaaa' then," Aaron said patiently. "You can't speak, but I know you understand. I need you and you need me. Isn't that right?"

"Maaaa."

Aaron became sleepy. He made a pillow out of some hay, leaned his head on it, and dozed off. Zlateh, too, fell asleep.

When Aaron opened his eyes, he didn't know whether it was morning or night. The snow had blocked up his window. He tried to clear it, but when he had bored through to the length of his arm, he still hadn't reached the outside. Luckily he had his stick with him and was able to break through to the open air. It was still dark outside. The snow continued to fall and the wind wailed, first with one voice and then with

---

exuded: gave off

many. Sometimes it had the sound of devilish laughter. Zlateh, too, awoke, and when Aaron greeted her, she answered, "Maaaa." Yes, Zlateh's language consisted of only one word, but it meant many things. Now she was saying, "We must accept all that God gives us—heat, cold, hunger, satisfaction, light, and darkness."

Aaron had awakened hungry. He had eaten up his food, but Zlateh had plenty of milk.

For three days Aaron and Zlateh stayed in the haystack. Aaron had always loved Zlateh, but in these three days he loved her more and more. She fed him with her milk and helped him keep warm. She comforted him with her patience. He told her many stories, and she always cocked her ears and listened. When he patted her, she licked his hand and his face. Then she said, "Maaaa," and he knew it meant, I love you, too.

The snow fell for three days, though after the first day it was not as thick and the wind quieted down. Sometimes Aaron felt that there could never have been a summer, that the snow had always fallen, ever since he could remember. He, Aaron, never had a father or mother or sisters. He was a snow child, born of the snow, and so was Zlateh. It was so quiet in the hay that his ears rang in the stillness. Aaron and Zlateh slept all night and a good part of the day. As for Aaron's dreams, they were all about warm weather. He dreamed of green fields, trees covered with blossoms, clear brooks, and singing birds. By the third night the snow had stopped, but Aaron did not dare to find his way home in the darkness. The sky became clear and the moon shone, casting silvery nets on the snow. Aaron dug his way out and looked at the world. It was all white, quiet, dreaming dreams of heavenly splendor. The stars were large and close. The moon swam in the sky as in a sea.

On the morning of the fourth day Aaron heard the ringing of sleigh bells. The haystack was not far from the road. The peasant who drove the sleigh pointed out the way to him— not to the town and Feivel the butcher, but home to the

---

splendor: great beauty or majesty

village. Aaron had decided in the haystack that he would never part with Zlateh.

Aaron's family and their neighbors had searched for the boy and the goat but had found no trace of them during the storm. They feared they were lost. Aaron's mother and sisters cried for him; his father remained silent and gloomy. Suddenly one of the neighbors came running to their house with the news that Aaron and Zlateh were coming up the road.

There was great joy in the family. Aaron told them how he had found the stack of hay and how Zlateh had fed him with her milk. Aaron's sisters kissed and hugged Zlateh and gave her a special treat of chopped carrots and potato peels, which Zlateh gobbled up hungrily.

Nobody ever again thought of selling Zlateh, and now that the cold weather had finally set in, the villagers needed the services of Reuven the furrier once more. When Hanukkah came, Aaron's mother was able to fry pancakes every evening, and Zlateh got her portion, too. Even though Zlateh had her own pen, she often came to the kitchen, knocking on the door with her horns to indicate that she was ready to visit, and she was always admitted. In the evening Aaron, Miriam, and Anna played dreidel. Zlateh sat near the stove watching the children and the flickering of the Hanukkah candles.

Once in a while Aaron would ask her, "Zlateh, do you remember the three days we spent together?"

And Zlateh would scratch her neck with a horn, shake her white bearded head, and come out with the single sound which expressed all her thoughts, and all her love.

---

dreidel: a Hanukkah game played with a spinning top, or the top itself

THE BLACK SNAKE
by Patricia Hubbell

Black snake! Black snake!
Curling on the ground,
Rolled like a rubber tire,
Ribbed and round.
Black snake! Black snake!
Looped in a tree,
Limp as a licorice whip
Flung free.
Black snake! Black snake!
Curving down the lawn,
Glides like a wave
With its silver gone.
Black snake! Black snake!
Come and live with me!
I'll feed you and I'll pet you
And then I'll set you free!

A NARROW FELLOW IN THE GRASS
by Emily Dickinson

A narrow Fellow in the Grass
Occasionally rides—
You may have met Him—did you not
His notice sudden is—

The Grass divides as with a Comb—
A spotted shaft is seen—
And then it closes at your feet
And opens further on—

He likes a Boggy Acre
A Floor too cool for Corn—
Yet when a Boy, and Barefoot—
I more than once at Noon

Have passed, I thought, a Whip lash
Unbraiding in the Sun
When stooping to secure it
It wrinkled, and was gone—

shaft: a spear or pole
boggy: wet or marshy
lash: the end of a whip
secure: to fasten in place

Several of Nature's People
I know, and they know me—
I feel for them a transport
Of cordiality—

But never met this Fellow
Attended, or alone
Without a tighter breathing
And Zero at the Bone—

---

transport: a strong emotion
cordiality: friendly courtesy

How a Cat Played
Robinson Crusoe

by Charles G. D. Roberts

I

The island was a mere sandbank off the low, flat coast. Not a tree broke its bleak levels—not even a shrub. But the long, gritty stalks of the marsh grass clothed it everywhere above tide mark, and a tiny rivulet of sweet water, flowing from a spring at its center, drew a ribbon of green across the harsh and somber yellow gray of the grass.

Few would have chosen the island as a place to live. Yet at its seaward end, where the changing tides were never still, stood a cottage, with a low shed behind it. When the mainland would be sweltering day and night, on the island there was always a cool wind blowing. And on this cool plot of sand, a wise city dweller had built his summer home.

The family came to the island toward the end of June. In the first week of September they went away, leaving every door and window of the house and shed securely shuttered, bolted, or barred against the winter's storms. A roomy boat, rowed by two fishermen, carried them across the half mile of racing tides that separated them from the mainland.

After two months of wind, sun, waves, and waving grass tops, the elders of the household were not sorry to get back to the world. But the children went with tear-stained faces.

---

bleak: grim
rivulet: a small river or stream
somber: serious
sweltering: unbearably hot

They were leaving behind them their favorite pet, a handsome, moonfaced cat, striped like a tiger. The animal had disappeared two days before, without leaving a trace behind. The only reasonable explanation seemed to be that she had been snapped up by a passing eagle. The cat, meanwhile, was a prisoner at the other end of the island, hidden beneath a broken barrel and drifted sand.

The old barrel, with the staves battered out of one side, had stood, half buried, on the crest of a sand ridge raised by a steady wind. Under it the cat had found a sheltered hollow, full of sun, where she liked to lie curled up for hours at a time, basking and sleeping. Meanwhile the sand had been steadily piling itself higher and higher behind the unstable barrier. At last it had piled too high, and suddenly, in response to a stronger gust, the barrel had come toppling over beneath a mass of sand, burying the sleeping cat out of sight and light. But at the same time the sound half of the barrel had formed a safe roof to her prison, and she was neither crushed nor smothered.

When the children in their anxious search all over the island chanced upon the mound of fine, white sand, they gave it but one careless look. They could not hear the faint cries that came, at intervals, from the darkness within. So they went away sorrowfully, little dreaming that their friend was imprisoned almost beneath their feet.

For three days the prisoner kept up her appeals for help. On the third day the wind changed and blew up a gale. In a few hours it had uncovered the barrel. At one corner a tiny spot of light appeared.

---

staves: strips of wood that form the sides of a barrel
basking: lying in and enjoying the warmth of

Eagerly the cat stuck her paw through the hole. When she withdrew it again the hole was much larger. She took the hint and fell to scratching. At first her efforts were rather aimless, but soon, whether by good luck or cleverness, she learned to make her scratching more effective. The opening rapidly enlarged, and at last she was able to squeeze her way out.

Filled with flying sand, the wind was tearing madly across the island. The seas hurled themselves trampling up the beach, with the uproar of a bombardment. The grasses lay bowed flat in long, quivering ranks. Over the turmoil the sun stared down from a deep, unclouded blue. The cat, when she first met the full force of the gale, was fairly blown off her feet. As soon as she could recover, she crouched low and

aimless: without direction
bombardment: an attack, as with cannons or bombs

darted for shelter. She sped straight before the gale, making for the cottage where she fondly imagined she would find not only food and shelter, but also loving comfort to make her forget her terrors.

Still and desolate in the bright sunshine and the tearing wind, the house frightened her. She could not understand the tight-closed shutters, or the blind, unresponding doors that would no longer open to her anxious appeal. The wind swept her savagely across the veranda. Climbing with difficulty to the dining room window sill, where so often she had been let in, she clung there a few moments and yowled heartbrokenly. Then, in a sudden panic, she jumped down and ran to the shed. That, too, was closed. Never before had she seen the shed doors closed, and she could not understand it. Cautiously she crept around the foundations— but there was no getting in that way. On every side it was nothing but a blank, forbidding face that the old familiar house confronted her with.

The cat had always been so coddled and pampered by the children that she had had no need to forage for herself. Fortunately for her, she had learned to hunt the marsh mice and grass sparrows for amusement. So now, ravenous from her long fast under the sand, she slunk mournfully away from the deserted house and crept along under the lee of a sand ridge to a little grassy hollow.

Here the gale caught only the tops of the grasses. And here, in the warmth and comparative calm, the mice and

---

savagely: fiercely
veranda: a porch
confronted: challenged
coddled: spoiled
forage: to search for food
ravenous: extremely hungry

shrews were going about their business undisturbed. The cat, quick and stealthy, soon caught one and eased her hunger. She caught several. And then, making her way back to the house, she spent hours in heartsick prowling, sniffing and peering, yowling piteously on threshold and windowsill. At last, hopelessly discouraged, she curled herself up beneath the children's window and went to sleep.

II

In spite of her loneliness and grief, the life of the island prisoner during the next two or three weeks was by no means one of hardship. Besides her abundant food of birds and mice, she quickly learned to catch tiny fish in the mouth of the rivulet, where salt water and fresh water met. It was an exciting game, and she became expert at dashing the gray tomcod and blue-and-silver sand lance far up the slope with a sweep of her armed paw.

But when the storms roared down upon the island, with furious rain, and low, black clouds torn to shreds, then life became more difficult for her. Game all took to cover, where it was hard to find. It was difficult to get around in the drenched and lashing grass, and she loathed being wet. Most of the time she went hungry, sitting sullen and desolate under the lee of the house, glaring out defiantly at the battling tumult of the waves.

The storm lasted nearly ten days. On the eighth day the abandoned wreck of a small schooner drove ashore. The battered hulk had passengers of a sort. A horde of rats got through the surf and scurried into the grass roots. They

lashing: moving in a violent, whip-like way
loathed: hated
sullen: sulky, gloomy
desolate: very lonely and joyless
tumult: commotion

promptly made themselves at home, burrowing under the dead grass, and carrying panic into the ranks of the mice and shrews.

When the storm was over, the cat had a surprise in her first long hunting expedition. Something had rustled the grass heavily, and she trailed it, expecting a particularly large, fat marsh mouse. When she pounced upon an immense old ship's rat, she got badly bitten. Such an experience had never before happened to her. At first she felt so injured that she was on the point of backing out and running away. Then the fire of far-off ancestors awoke within her. She flung herself furiously into the fight, and the struggle was soon over. Her wounds, faithfully licked, quickly healed in that clean and healthy air. After that, having learned how to handle such big game, she got bitten no more.

During the first full moon after her abandonment—the first week in October—the island was visited by still weather with sharp night frosts. The cat discovered then that it was most exciting to hunt by night and do her sleeping in the daytime. She found that now, under the strange whiteness of the moon, all her game was astir—except the birds, which had fled to the mainland during the storm, gathering for the southward flight. Everywhere the blanched grasses rustled, and everywhere dim little shapes went darting with thin squeaks across ghostly white sands. Also she made the acquaintance of a new bird, which she regarded at first uneasily and then with vengeful wrath. This was the brown marsh owl, which came over from the mainland to do some autumn mouse hunting. There were two pairs of these big, downy-winged, round-eyed hunters, and they did not know there was a cat on the island.

---

vengeful: seeking revenge; eager to get even or get back at

The cat, spying one of them as it swooped soundlessly over the silvered grass, crouched with flattened ears. With its wide spread of wing and its great round face with hooked beak and wild, staring eyes, it appeared very threatening. However, she was no coward; and soon, she went about her hunting, though cautiously. Suddenly, the owl caught a partial glimpse of her ears in the grass. He swooped, and at the same instant she sprang upward to meet the assault, spitting and growling harshly, and striking with unsheathed claws. With a frantic flapping of his great wings the owl checked himself and drew back into the air. After that the marsh owls realized that it was best not to interfere with the black-striped animal with the quick spring and the clutching claws.

III

Winter deepened, with bursts of sharp cold and changing winds that forced the cat continually to seek new refuge. She grew more and more unhappy, and felt her homelessness keenly. Nowhere on the whole island could she find a nook where she might feel secure from both wind and rain. As for the old barrel, the first cause of her misfortunes, there was no help in that. The winds had long ago turned it completely over, open to the sky, then drifted it full of sand and reburied it. And in any case, the cat would have been afraid to go near it again.

So it came about that she alone of all the island dwellers had no shelter when the real winter arrived, with snows that smothered the grass tops out of sight, and frosts that lined the shore with grinding ice cakes. The rats had their holes under the buried fragments of wreckage; the mice and

---

refuge: a safe place
keenly: sharply

shrews had their deep, warm tunnels; the owls had nests in hollow trees far away in the forests of the mainland. But the cat, shivering and frightened, could do nothing but crouch against the blind walls of the unrelenting house and let the snow whirl itself about her.

And now, in her misery, she found her food cut off. The mice ran secure in their hidden runways, where the grass roots on each side gave them easy and abundant food. The rats, too, were out of sight, digging burrows in the soft snow. The ice fringe, crumbling and heaving under the ruthless tide, put an end to her fishing. She would have tried to capture one of the formidable owls in her hunger, but the owls no longer came to the island, as they were following an easier chase in the deeps of the upland forest.

When the snow stopped and the sun came out again, there fell such keen cold as the cat had never felt before. The day, as it chanced, was Christmas; and if the cat had had any idea of the calendar she would certainly have marked the day in her memory, as it proved to be an important one for her.

Starving as she was, she could not sleep, but kept ceaselessly on the prowl. This was fortunate, for had she gone to sleep with no more shelter than the wall of the house, she would never have awakened again. In her restlessness she wandered to the farther side of the island where, in a sunny recess of the shore facing the mainland, she found a patch of bare sand, free of ice cakes and just uncovered by the tide. Opening upon this recess were the tiny entrances to several of the mouse tunnels.

Close beside one of these holes in the snow the cat crouched, quivering, intent. For ten minutes or more she

---

formidable: inspiring awe, wonder, or fear
intent: focused on some purpose

waited, never so much as twitching a whisker. At last a mouse thrust out its little pointed head. Not daring to give it time to change its mind or take alarm, she pounced. The mouse doubled back into the narrow runway. Hardly realizing what she did in her desperation, the cat plunged head and shoulders into the snow, reaching blindly after the vanished prize. By great good luck she caught it. It was her first meal in four bitter days.

Now she had learned a lesson. Being naturally clever, and her wits being sharpened by fierce necessity, she understood that it was possible to follow her prey a little way into the snow. Since she had wiped out the door of this particular runway, she went and crouched beside a similar one, but here she had to wait a long time before an adventurous mouse came to peer out. But this time she showed that she had learned her lesson. She pounced straight at the side of the entrance, where instinct told her that the body of the mouse would be. One outstretched paw thus cut off the quarry's retreat. Her tactics were successful—as her head went plunging into the fluffy whiteness, she felt the prize between her paws.

Her hunger appeased, she found herself immensely excited over this new way of hunting. Often before had she waited at mouse holes, but never had she found it possible to break down the walls and invade the holes themselves. It was a thrilling idea. As she crept toward another hole a mouse scurried swiftly up the sand and darted into it. The cat, too late to catch him before he disappeared, tried to follow him. Scratching clumsily but hopefully, she succeeded in forcing the full length of her body into the snow. She

------

quarry: prey; an animal hunted or chased
appeased: calmed; soothed; satisfied

found no sign of the fugitive, which was by this time racing in safety down some dim tunnel. With her eyes, mouth, whiskers, and fur full of powdery white particles, she backed out, much disappointed. But in that moment she realized it was much warmer in there beneath the snow than out in the stinging air. It was a second vitally important lesson that she instinctively put into practice a little while later.

IV

She caught yet another mouse and carried it back to the house. She laid it down in tribute on the veranda steps while she meowed and stared hopefully at the desolate, snow-draped door. Getting no response, she carried the mouse down to the hollow behind a drift caused by the bulging bay window on the end of the house. Here she curled herself up forlornly, thinking to have a wink of sleep.

But the still cold was too biting. She looked at the sloping wall of snow beside her and cautiously thrust her paw into it. It was very soft and light. It seemed to offer very little resistance. She pawed away in an awkward fashion till she had scooped out a sort of tiny cave. Gently she pushed herself into it, pressing back the snow on every side till she had room to turn around. Then turn around she did several times, as dogs do in getting their beds arranged to their liking.

In this way she not only packed down the snow beneath her, but she also rounded out for herself a snug chamber with a narrow doorway. From this snowy retreat she gazed forth with a solemn air of possession; then she went to sleep with a sense of comfort, of "homeyness," such as she had never before felt since the disappearance of her friends.

From now on, her life in the winter wild, though strenuous, was no longer one of any terrible hardship. With patience at the mouse holes she could catch enough to eat. In her snowy den she slept warm and secure. In a little while, when a crust had formed over the surface of the snow, the mice took to coming out at night. Then the owls, too, came back. The cat tried to catch one, but got sharply bitten and clawed before she let it go. After this she decided that owls were meant to be let alone. But still she enjoyed fine hunting out there on the bleak, white reaches of the snow.

When spring came back to the island, with the nightly shrill chorus of frogs in the shallow pools, and the young grass alive with nesting birds, the prisoner's life became almost pleasant in its easy abundance. But now she was once more homeless, since her snug den had vanished with the snow. This did not much matter, however, for the weather grew warmer and more tranquil day by day. And she herself, in being forced back upon her instincts, had learned to be contented. Nevertheless, with all her capacity for learning and adapting herself, she had not forgotten anything.

One day in June, a crowded boat arrived from the mainland, and children's voices came clamoring across the grass tops, breaking the desolate silence of the island. The cat heard and sprang up out of her sleep on the veranda steps.

For one second she stood, listening intently. Then, almost as a dog would do, and as few of her tribe ever condescend to do, she went racing across to the landing place—to be snatched up into the arms of four happy children at once, and to have her fine fur ruffled to a state that would cost her an hour's careful grooming to put in order.

---

strenuous: requiring great effort
condescend: to lower oneself

ODE TO MI GATO
by Gary Soto

He's white
As spilled milk,
My cat who sleeps
With his belly
Turned toward
The summer sky.
He loves the sun,
Its warmth like a hand.
He loves tuna cans
And milk cartons
With their dribble
Of milk. He loves
Mom when she rattles
The bag of cat food,
The brown nuggets
Raining into his bowl.
And my cat loves
Me, because I saved
Him from a dog,
Because I dressed him
In a hat and a cape
For Halloween,
Because I dangled
A sock of chicken skin

ode: a poem of praise
mi gato: Spanish for "my cat"

And he stood on his
Hind legs. I love mi gato,
Porque I found
Him on the fender
Of an abandoned car.
He was a kitten,
With a meow
Like the rusty latch
On a gate. I carried
Him home in the loop
Of my arms.
I poured milk
Into him, let him
Lick chunks of
Cheese from my palms,
And cooked huevo
After huevo
Until his purring
Engine kicked in
And he cuddled
Up to my father's slippers.
That was last year.
This spring,
He's excellent at sleeping

---

porque: Spanish for "because"
huevo: Spanish for "egg"

And no good
At hunting. At night
All the other cats
In the neighborhood
Can see him slink
Around the corner,
Or jump from the tree
Like a splash of
Milk. We lap up
His love and
He laps up his welcome.

THE OPEN DOOR
by Elizabeth Coatsworth

Out of the dark
to the sill of the door
lay the snow in a long
unruffled floor,
and the lamplight fell
narrow and thin
a carpet unrolled
for the cat to walk in.
Slowly, smoothly,
Black as the night,
with paws unseen
(white upon white)
like a queen who walks
down a corridor
the black cat paced
that cold smooth floor—
and left behind her,
bead upon bead,
the track of small feet
like dark fern seed.

---

unruffled: not wrinkled; smooth and flat
corridor: a hallway

THE CAT AND THE MOON
by William Butler Yeats

The cat went here and there
And the moon spun round like a top,
And the nearest kin of the moon,
The creeping cat, looked up.
Black Minnaloushe stared at the moon,
For, wander and wail as he would,
The pure cold light in the sky
Troubled his animal blood.
Minnaloushe runs in the grass
Lifting his delicate feet.
Do you dance, Minnaloushe, do you dance?
When two close kindred meet,
What better than call a dance?
Maybe the moon may learn,
Tired of that courtly fashion,
A new dance turn.
Minnaloushe creeps through the grass
From moonlit place to place,
The sacred moon overhead
Has taken a new phase.

---

kin: a relative; a family member
wail: to cry loudly
kindred: relatives; family members
courtly: noble or elegant

Does Minnaloushe know that his pupils
Will pass from change to change,
And that from round to crescent,
From crescent to round they range?
Minnaloushe creeps through the grass
Alone, important and wise,
And lifts to the changing moon
His changing eyes.

pupils: centers of the eyes
crescent: the shape of a moon when it is very thin

THE NAMING OF CATS
by T. S. Eliot

The Naming of Cats is a difficult matter,
    It isn't just one of your holiday games;
You may think at first I'm as mad as a hatter
    When I tell you, a cat must have
    THREE DIFFERENT NAMES.
First of all, there's the name that the family use daily,
    Such as Peter, Augustus, Alonzo or James,
Such as Victor or Jonathan, George or Bill Bailey—
    All of them sensible everyday names.
There are fancier names if you think they sound sweeter,
    Some for the gentlemen, some for the dames:
Such as Plato, Admetus, Electra, Demeter—
    But all of them sensible everyday names.
But I tell you, a cat needs a name that's particular,
    A name that's peculiar, and more dignified,
Else how can he keep up his tail perpendicular,
    Or spread out his whiskers, or cherish his pride?
Of names of this kind, I can give you a quorum,
    Such as Munkustrap, Quaxo, or Coricopat,
Such as Bombalurina, or else Jellylorum—
    Names that never belonged to more than one cat.

---

hatter: a person who makes, sells, and fixes hats, such as the Mad Hatter
    character in *Alice's Adventures in Wonderland*
dames: women
perpendicular: standing upright; creating a right angle
cherish: to hold dear
quorum: a group

But above and beyond there's still one name left over,
   And that is the name that you never will guess;
The name that no human research can discover—
   But THE CAT HIMSELF KNOWS, and will never confess.
When you notice a cat in profound meditation,
   The reason, I tell you, is always the same:
His mind is engaged in a rapt contemplation
   Of the thought, of the thought, of the thought of his name:
   His ineffable effable
   Effanineffable
Deep and inscrutable singular Name.

---

profound: deep
meditation: thought
rapt: with attention completely engaged
contemplation: deeply focused thinking
ineffable: beyond expression; incapable of being put into words
inscrutable: mysterious; difficult to understand

THE RUM TUM TUGGER
by T. S. Eliot

The Rum Tum Tugger is a Curious Cat:
If you offer him pheasant he would rather have grouse.
If you put him in a house he would much prefer a flat,
If you put him in a flat then he'd rather have a house.
If you set him on a mouse then he only wants a rat,
If you set him on a rat then he'd rather chase a mouse.
Yes the Rum Tum Tugger is a Curious Cat—
   And there isn't any call for me to shout it:
      For he will do
      As he do do
         And there's no doing anything about it!

The Rum Tum Tugger is a terrible bore:
When you let him in, then he wants to be out;
He's always on the wrong side of every door,
And as soon as he's at home, then he'd like to get about.
He likes to lie in the bureau drawer,
But he makes such a fuss if he can't get out.
Yes the Rum Tum Tugger is a Curious Cat—
   And it isn't any use for you to doubt it:
      For he will do
      As he do do
         And there's no doing anything about it!

---

grouse: a kind of small bird
flat: an apartment

The Rum Tum Tugger is a curious beast:
His disobliging ways are a matter of habit.
If you offer him fish then he always wants a feast;
When there isn't any fish then he won't eat rabbit.
If you offer him cream then he sniffs and sneers,
For he only likes what he finds for himself;
So you'll catch him in it right up to the ears,
If you put it away on the larder shelf.
The Rum Tum Tugger is artful and knowing,
The Rum Tum Tugger doesn't care for a cuddle;
But he'll leap on your lap in the middle of your sewing,
For there's nothing he enjoys like a horrible muddle.
Yes the Rum Tum Tugger is a Curious Cat—
    And there isn't any need for me to spout it:
        For he will do
        As he do do
            And there's no doing anything about it!

---

disobliging: going against someone's wishes
larder: a pantry
muddle: a mess; a state of disorder and confusion

STRAY

by Cynthia Rylant

In January, a puppy wandered onto the property of Mr. Amos Lacey and his wife, Mamie, and their daughter, Doris. Icicles hung three feet or more from the eaves of houses, snowdrifts swallowed up automobiles, and the birds were so fluffed up they looked comic.

The puppy had been abandoned, and it made its way down the road toward the Laceys' small house, its ears tucked, its tail between its legs, shivering.

Doris, whose school had been called off because of the snow, was out shoveling the cinder-block front steps when she spotted the pup on the road. She set down the shovel.

"Hey! Come on!" she called.

The puppy stopped in the road, wagging its tail timidly, trembling with shyness and cold.

Doris trudged through the yard, went up the shoveled drive, and met the dog.

"Come on, pooch."

"Where did that come from?" Mrs. Lacey asked as soon as Doris put the dog down in the kitchen.

Mr. Lacey was at the table, cleaning his fingernails with his pocketknife. The snow was keeping him home from his job at the warehouse.

"I don't know where it came from," he said mildly, "but I know for sure where it's going."

Doris hugged the puppy hard against her. She said nothing.

---

eaves: the part of a roof that hangs over the wall

Because the roads would be too bad for travel for many days, Mr. Lacey couldn't get out to take the puppy to the pound in the city right away. He agreed to let it sleep in the basement, while Mrs. Lacey grudgingly let Doris feed it table scraps. The woman was sensitive about throwing out food.

By the looks of it, Doris figured the puppy was about six months old and on its way to a big dog. She thought it might have some shepherd in it.

Four days passed and the puppy did not complain. It never cried in the night or howled at the wind. It didn't tear up everything in the basement. It wouldn't even follow Doris up the basement steps unless it was invited.

It was a good dog.

Several times Doris had opened the door in the kitchen that led to the basement, and the puppy had been there, all stretched out, on the top step. Doris knew it had wanted some company and that it had lain against the door, listening to the talk in the kitchen, smelling the food, being a part of things. It always wagged its tail, eyes all sleepy, when she found it there.

Even after a week had gone by, Doris didn't name the dog. She knew her parents wouldn't let her keep it, that her father made so little money any pets were out of the question, and that the pup would definitely go to the pound when the weather cleared. Still, she tried talking to them about the dog at dinner one night.

"She's a good dog, isn't she?" Doris said, hoping one of them would agree with her.

---

grudgingly: reluctantly, unwillingly

Her parents glanced at each other and went on eating.

"She's not much trouble," Doris added. "I like her." She smiled at them, but they continued to ignore her.

"I figure she's real smart," Doris said to her mother. "I could teach her things."

Mrs. Lacey just shook her head and stuffed a forkful of sweet potato in her mouth. Doris fell silent, praying the weather would never clear.

But on Saturday, nine days after the dog had arrived, the sun was shining and the roads were plowed. Mr. Lacey opened up the trunk of his car and came into the house.

Doris was sitting alone in the living room, hugging a pillow and rocking back and forth on the edge of a chair. She was trying not to cry but she was not strong enough. Her face was wet and red, her eyes full of distress.

Mrs. Lacey looked into the room from the doorway.

"Mama," Doris said in a small voice. "Please."

Mrs. Lacey shook her head.

"You know we can't afford a dog, Doris. You try to act more grown-up about this."

Doris pressed her face into the pillow.

Outside, she heard the trunk of the car slam shut, one of the doors open and close, the old engine cough and choke and finally start up.

"Daddy," she whispered. "Please."

She heard the car travel down the road, and though it was early afternoon, she could do nothing but go to her bed. She cried herself to sleep, and her dreams were full of searching and searching for things lost.

It was nearly night when she finally woke up. Lying there, like stone, still exhausted, she wondered if she would ever in her life have anything. She stared at the wall for a while.

But she started feeling hungry, and she knew she'd have to make herself get out of bed and eat some dinner. She wanted not to go into the kitchen, past the basement door. She wanted not to face her parents.

But she rose up heavily.

Her parents were sitting at the table, dinner over, drinking coffee. They looked at her when she came in, but she kept her head down. No one spoke.

Doris made herself a glass of powdered milk and drank it all down. Then she picked up a cold biscuit and started out of the room.

"You'd better feed that mutt before it dies of starvation," Mr. Lacey said.

Doris turned around.

"What?"

"I said, you'd better feed your dog. I figure it's looking for you."

Doris put her hand to her mouth.

"You didn't take her?" she asked.

"Oh, I took her all right," her father answered. "Worst-looking place I've ever seen. Ten dogs to a cage. Smell was enough to knock you down. And they give an animal six days to live. Then they kill it with some kind of a shot."

Doris stared at her father.

"I wouldn't leave an ant in that place," he said. "So I brought the dog back."

Mrs. Lacey was smiling at him and shaking her head as if she would never, ever, understand him.

Mr. Lacey sipped his coffee.

"Well," he said, "are you going to feed it or not?"

LONE DOG

by Irene Rutherford McLeod

I'm a lean dog, a keen dog, a wild dog, and lone;
I'm a rough dog, a tough dog, hunting on my own;
I'm a bad dog, a mad dog, teasing silly sheep;
I love to sit and bay the moon, to keep fat souls from sleep.
I'll never be a lap dog, licking dirty feet,
A sleek dog, a meek dog, cringing for my meat,
Not for me the fireside, the well-filled plate,
But shut door, and sharp stone, and cuff, and kick, and hate.
Not for me the other dogs, running by my side,
Some have run a short while, but none of them would bide.
O mine is still the lone trail, the hard trail, the best,
Wide wind, and wild stars, and the hunger of the quest!

keen: sharp; clever
bay: to howl
cringing: shrinking in fear
cuff: a slap
bide: to last

VERN

by Gwendolyn Brooks

When walking in a tiny rain
Across the vacant lot,
A pup's a good companion—
If a pup you've got.
And when you've had a scold,
And no one loves you very,
And you cannot be merry,
A pup will let you look at him,
And even let you hold
His little wiggly warmness—
And let you snuggle down beside.
Nor mock the tears you have to hide.

---

vacant: empty

The Dog of Pompeii
by Louis Untermeyer

Tito and his dog Bimbo lived (if you could call it living) under the wall where it joined the inner gate. They really didn't live there; they just slept there. They lived anywhere. Pompeii was one of the gayest of the old Latin towns, but although Tito was never an unhappy boy, he was not exactly a merry one. The streets were always lively with shining chariots and bright red trappings; the open-air theaters rocked with laughing crowds; sham battles and athletic sports were free for the asking in the great stadium. Once a year the Caesar visited the pleasure city and the fireworks lasted for days; the sacrifices in the forum were better than a show.

But Tito saw none of these things. He was blind—had been blind from birth. He was known to everyone in the poorer quarters. But no one could say how old he was, no one remembered his parents, no one could tell where he came from. Bimbo was another mystery. As long as people could remember seeing Tito—about twelve or thirteen years— they had seen Bimbo. Bimbo had never left his side. He was not only dog but nurse, pillow, playmate, mother, and father to Tito.

Did I say Bimbo never left his master? (Perhaps I had better say comrade, for if anyone was the master, it was

---

trappings: decorations
sham: fake; pretend
Caesar: a Roman emperor
forum: the marketplace or central meeting place of an ancient Roman city

Bimbo.) I was wrong. Bimbo did trust Tito alone exactly three times a day. It was a fixed routine, a custom understood between boy and dog since the beginning of their friendship, and the way it worked was this:

Early in the morning, shortly after dawn, while Tito was still dreaming, Bimbo would disappear. When Tito awoke, Bimbo would be sitting quietly at his side, his ears cocked, his stump of a tail tapping the ground, and a fresh-baked bread—more like a large round roll— at his feet. Tito would stretch himself; Bimbo would yawn; then they would breakfast. At noon, no matter where they happened to be, Bimbo would put his paw on Tito's knee and the two of them would return to the inner gate. Tito would curl up in the corner (almost like a dog) and go to sleep, while Bimbo, looking quite important (almost like a boy), would disappear again. In half an hour he'd be back with their lunch. Sometimes it would be a piece of fruit or a scrap of meat, often it was nothing but a dry crust. But sometimes there would be one of those flat rich cakes, sprinkled with raisins and sugar, that Tito liked so much. At suppertime the same thing happened, although there was a little less of everything, for things were hard to snatch in the evening, with the streets full of people. Besides, Bimbo didn't approve of too much food before going to sleep. A heavy supper made boys too restless and dogs too stodgy—and it was the business of a dog to sleep lightly with one ear open and muscles ready for action.

---

stodgy: heavy and slow

But, whether there was much or little, hot or cold, fresh or dry, food was always there. Tito never asked where it came from and Bimbo never told him. There was plenty of rainwater in the hollows of soft stones; the old egg woman at the corner sometimes gave him a cupful of strong goat's milk; in the grape season the fat winemaker let him have drippings of the mild juice. So there was no danger of going hungry or thirsty. There was plenty of everything in Pompeii—if you knew where to find it—and if you had a dog like Bimbo.

As I said before, Tito was not the merriest boy in Pompeii. He could not romp with the other youngsters and play "hare and hounds" and "I spy" and "follow your master" and "ball against the building" and "jackstones" and "kings and robbers" with them. But that did not make him sorry for himself. If he could not see the sights that delighted the lads of Pompeii, he could hear and smell things they never noticed. He could really see more with his ears and nose than they could with their eyes. When he and Bimbo went out walking, he knew just where they were going and exactly what was happening.

"Ah," he'd sniff and say, as they passed a handsome villa, "Glaucus Pansa is giving a grand dinner tonight. They're going to have three kinds of bread, and roast pigling, and stuffed goose, and a great stew—I think bear stew—and a fig pie." And Bimbo would note that this would be a good place to visit tomorrow.

Or, "H'm," Tito would murmur, half through his lips, half through his nostrils. "The wife of Marcus Lucretius is expecting her mother. She's shaking out every piece of goods in the house; she's going to use the best clothes—the ones

---

villa: a large house

she's been keeping in pine needles and camphor—and there's an extra girl in the kitchen. Come, Bimbo, let's get out of the dust!"

Or, as they passed a small but elegant dwelling opposite the public baths, "Too bad! The tragic poet is ill again. It must be a bad fever this time, for they're trying smoke fumes instead of medicine. Whew! I'm glad I'm not a tragic poet!"

Or, as they neared the forum, "Mm-m! What good things they have in the macellum today!" (It really was a sort of butcher-grocer-marketplace, but Tito didn't know any better. He called it the macellum.) "Dates from Africa, and salt oysters from sea caves, and cuttlefish, and new honey, and sweet onions, and—ugh!—water-buffalo steaks. Come, let's see what's what in the forum." And Bimbo, just as curious as his comrade, hurried on. Being a dog, he trusted his ears and nose (like Tito) more than his eyes. And so the two of them entered the center of Pompeii.

The forum was the part of the town to which everybody came at least once during the day. It was the central square, and everything happened here. There were no private houses; all was public—the chief temples, the gold and red bazaars, the silk shops, the town hall, the booths belonging to the weavers and jewel merchants, the wealthy woolen market, the shrine of the household gods. Everything glittered here. The buildings looked as if they were new—which, in a sense, they were. The earthquake of twelve years ago had brought down all the old structures and, since the citizens of Pompeii were ambitious to rival Naples and even

---

camphor: a strong smelling substance that keeps moths away
tragic poet: a poet who often writes about sad events or a hero's downfall
ambitious: having a strong desire to achieve a goal; eager for
    power or fame

Rome, they had seized the opportunity to rebuild the whole town. And they had done it all within a dozen years. There was scarcely a building that was older than Tito.

Tito had heard a great deal about the earthquake, though being about a year old at the time, he could scarcely remember it. This particular quake had been a light one—as earthquakes go. The weaker houses had been shaken down, parts of the outworn wall had been wrecked; but there was little loss of life, and the brilliant new Pompeii had taken the place of the old. No one knew what caused these earthquakes. Records showed they had happened in the neighborhood since the beginning of time. Sailors said that it was to teach the lazy city folk a lesson and make them appreciate those who risked the dangers of the sea to bring them luxuries and protect their town from invaders. The priests said that the gods took this way of showing their anger to those who refused to worship properly and who failed to bring enough sacrifices to the altars and (though they didn't say it in so many words) presents to the priests. The tradesmen said that the foreign merchants had corrupted the ground and it was no longer safe to traffic in imported goods that came from strange places and carried a curse with them. Everyone had a different explanation and everyone's explanation was louder and sillier than his neighbor's.

They were talking about it this afternoon as Tito and Bimbo came out of the side street into the public square. The forum was the favorite promenade for rich and poor. What with the priests arguing with the politicians, servants doing the day's shopping, tradesmen crying their wares, women displaying the latest fashions from Greece and Egypt, children playing hide-and-seek among the marble columns, knots of soldiers, sailors, peasants from the provinces—to say nothing of those who merely came to lounge and look on—the square was crowded to its last inch. His ears even more than his nose guided Tito to the place where the talk was loudest. It was in front of the shrine of the household gods that, naturally enough, the householders were arguing.

"I tell you," rumbled a voice which Tito recognized as bath master Rufus's, "there won't be another earthquake in my lifetime or yours. There may be a tremble or two, but earthquakes, like lightnings, never strike twice in the same place."

"Do they not?" asked a thin voice Tito had never heard. It had a high, sharp ring to it and Tito knew it as the accent of a stranger. "How about the two towns of Sicily that have been ruined three times within fifteen years by the eruptions of Mount Etna? And were they not warned? And does that column of smoke above Vesuvius mean nothing?"

"That?" Tito could hear the grunt with which one question answered another. "That's always there. We use it for our weather guide. When the smoke stands up straight, we know we'll have fair weather; when it flattens out, it's sure to be foggy; when it drifts to the east—"

"Yes, yes," cut in the edged voice. "I've heard about your mountain barometer. But the column of smoke seems hundreds of feet higher than usual and it's thickening and spreading like a shadowy tree. They say in Naples—"

"Oh, Naples!" Tito knew this voice by the little squeak that went with it. It was Attilio the cameo cutter. "They talk while we suffer. Little help we got from them last time. Naples commits the crimes and Pompeii pays the price. It's become a proverb with us. Let them mind their own business."

---

cameo: a small ornament with a sculpture of person's head

"Yes," grumbled Rufus, "and others', too."

"Very well, my confident friends," responded the thin voice, which now sounded curiously flat. "We also have a proverb—and it is this: Those who will not listen to men must be taught by the gods. I say no more. But I leave a last warning. Remember the holy ones. Look to your temples. And when the smoke tree above Vesuvius grows to the shape of an umbrella pine, look to your lives."

Tito could hear the air whistle as the speaker drew his toga about him, and the quick shuffle of feet told him the stranger had gone.

"Now what," said the cameo cutter, "did he mean by that?"

"I wonder," grunted Rufus. "I wonder."

Tito wondered, too. And Bimbo, his head at a thoughtful angle, looked as if he had been doing a heavy piece of pondering. By nightfall the argument had been forgotten. If the smoke had increased, no one saw it in the dark. Besides, it was Caesar's birthday and the town was in a holiday mood. Tito and Bimbo were among the merrymakers, dodging the charioteers who shouted at them. A dozen times they almost upset baskets of sweets and jars of Vesuvian wine, said to be as fiery as the streams inside the volcano, and a dozen times they were cursed and cuffed. But Tito never missed his footing. He was thankful for his keen ears and quick instinct—most thankful of all for Bimbo.

They visited the uncovered theater, and though Tito could not see the faces of the actors, he could follow the play better than most of the audience, for their attention wandered— they were distracted by the scenery, the costumes, the byplay, even by themselves—while Tito's whole attention was centered in what he heard. Then to the city walls, where the people of Pompeii watched a mock naval battle in which the city was attacked by the sea and saved after thousands of flaming arrows had been exchanged and countless colored torches had been burned. Though the thrill of flaring ships and lighted skies was lost to Tito, the shouts and cheers excited him as much as any, and he cried out with the loudest of them.

---

toga: a loose robe worn by the citizens of ancient Rome

The next morning there were two of the beloved raisin-and-sugar cakes for his breakfast. Bimbo was unusually active and thumped his bit of a tail until Tito was afraid he would wear it out. The boy could not imagine whether Bimbo was urging him to some sort of game or was trying to tell him something. After a while, he ceased to notice Bimbo. He felt drowsy. Last night's late hours had tired him. Besides, there was a heavy mist in the air—no, a thick fog rather than a mist—a fog that got into his throat and scraped it and made him cough. He walked as far as the marine gate to get a breath of the sea. But the blanket of haze had spread all over the bay and even the salt air seemed smoky.

He went to bed before dusk and slept. But he did not sleep well. He had too many dreams—dreams of ships lurching in the forum, of losing his way in a screaming crowd, of armies marching across his chest, of being pulled over every rough pavement of Pompeii.

He woke early. Or, rather, he was pulled awake. Bimbo was doing the pulling. The dog had dragged Tito to his feet and was urging the boy along. Somewhere. Where, Tito did not know. His feet stumbled uncertainly; he was still half asleep. For a while he noticed nothing except the fact that it was hard to breathe. The air was hot. And heavy. So heavy that he could taste it. The air, it seemed, had turned to powder—a warm powder that stung his nostrils and burned his sightless eyes.

Then he began to hear sounds. Peculiar sounds. Like animals under the earth. Hissings and groanings and muffled cries that a dying creature might make dislodging the stones of his underground cave. There was no doubt of it now. The noises came from underneath. He not only heard them—he could feel them. The earth twitched; the twitching changed to an uneven shrugging of the soil. Then, as Bimbo half pulled, half coaxed him across, the ground jerked away from his feet and he was thrown against a stone fountain.

The water—hot water—splashing in his face revived him. He got to his feet, Bimbo steadying him, helping him on again. The noises grew louder; they came closer. The cries were even more animal-like than before, but now they came from human throats. A few people, quicker of foot and more hurried by fear, began to rush by. A family or two—then a section—then, it seemed, an army broken out of bounds. Tito, bewildered though he was, could recognize Rufus as he bellowed past him, like a water buffalo gone mad. Time was lost in a nightmare.

It was then the crashing began. First a sharp crackling, like a monstrous snapping of twigs; then a roar like the fall of a whole forest of trees; then an explosion that tore earth and sky. The heavens, though Tito could not see them, were shot through with continual flickerings of fire. Lightnings above were answered by thunders beneath. A house fell. Then another. By a miracle the two companions had escaped the dangerous side streets and were in a more open space. It was the forum. They rested here awhile—how long, he did not know.

Tito had no idea of the time of day. He could feel it was black—an unnatural blackness. Something inside—perhaps the lack of breakfast and lunch—told him it was past noon. But it didn't matter. Nothing seemed to matter. He was getting drowsy, too drowsy to walk, but walk he must. He knew it. And Bimbo knew it; the sharp tugs told him so. Nor was it a moment too soon. The sacred ground of the forum was safe no longer. It was beginning to rock, then to pitch,

---

coaxed: urged

then to split. As they stumbled out of the square, the earth wriggled like a caught snake and all the columns of the temple of Jupiter came down. It was the end of the world—or so it seemed. To walk was not enough now. They must run. Tito was too frightened to know what to do or where to go. He had lost all sense of direction. He started to go back to the inner gate; but Bimbo, straining his back to the last inch, almost pulled his clothes from him. What did the creature want? Had the dog gone mad?

Then suddenly he understood. Bimbo was telling him the way out—urging him there. The sea gate, of course. The sea gate—and then the sea. Far from falling buildings, heaving ground. He turned, Bimbo guiding him across open pits and dangerous pools of bubbling mud, away from buildings that had caught fire and were dropping their burning beams. Tito could no longer tell whether the noises were made by the shrieking sky or the agonized people. He and Bimbo ran on—the only silent beings in a howling world.

New dangers threatened. All Pompeii seemed to be thronging toward the marine gate and, squeezing among the crowds, there was the chance of being trampled to death. But the chance had to be taken. It was growing harder and harder to breathe. What air there was choked him. It was all dust now—dust and pebbles, pebbles as large as beans. They fell on his head, his hands—pumice stones from the black heart of Vesuvius. The mountain was turning itself inside out. Tito remembered a phrase that the stranger had said in the forum two days ago: "Those who will not listen to men must be taught by the gods." The people of Pompeii had refused to heed the warnings; they were being taught now—if it was not too late.

Jupiter: in the ancient Roman religion, the king of the gods

Suddenly it seemed too late for Tito. The red-hot ashes blistered his skin, the stinging vapors tore his throat. He could not go on. He staggered toward a small tree at the side of the road and fell. In a moment Bimbo was beside him. He coaxed. But there was no answer. He licked Tito's hands, his feet, his face. The boy did not stir. Then Bimbo did the last thing he could—the last thing he wanted to do. He bit his comrade, bit him deep in the arm. With a cry of pain, Tito jumped to his feet, Bimbo after him. Tito was in despair, but Bimbo was determined. He drove the boy on, snapping at his heels, worrying his way through the crowd, barking, baring his teeth, heedless of kicks or falling stones. Sick with hunger, half dead with fear and sulfur fumes, Tito pounded on, pursued by Bimbo. How long, he never knew. At last he staggered through the marine gate and felt soft sand under him. Then Tito fainted....

Someone was dashing seawater over him. Someone was carrying him toward a boat.

"Bimbo," he called. And then louder, "Bimbo!" But Bimbo had disappeared.

Voices jarred against each other. "Hurry— hurry!" "To the boats!" "Can't you see the child's frightened and starving!" "He keeps calling for someone!" "Poor boy, he's out of his mind." "Here, child—take this!"

They tucked him in among them. The oarlocks creaked; the oars splashed; the boat rode over toppling waves. Tito was safe. But he wept continually.

"Bimbo!" he wailed. "Bimbo! Bimbo!"

He could not be comforted.

* * * * *

Eighteen hundred years passed. Scientists were restoring the ancient city; excavators were working their way through the stones and trash that had buried the entire town. Much had already been brought to light—statues, bronze instruments, bright mosaics, household articles; even delicate paintings had been preserved by the fall of ashes that had taken over two thousand lives. Columns were dug up, and the forum was beginning to emerge.

It was at a place where the ruins lay deepest that the director paused.

"Come here," he called to his assistant. "I think we've discovered the remains of a building in good shape. Here are four huge millstones that were most likely turned by slaves or mules—and here is a whole wall standing with shelves inside it. Why! It must have been a bakery. And here's a curious thing. What do you think I found under this heap where the ashes were thickest? The skeleton of a dog!"

"Amazing!" gasped his assistant. "You'd think a dog would have had sense enough to run away at the time. And what is that flat thing he's holding between his teeth? It can't be a stone."

"No. It must have come from this bakery. You know it looks to me like some sort of cake hardened with the years. And, bless me, if those little black pebbles aren't raisins. A raisin cake almost two thousand years old! I wonder what made him want it at such a moment."

"I wonder," murmured the assistant.

---

mosaics: designs made of small bits of glass, tile, or stone

LIFE STORIES: CREATIVE LIVES

The Child of Urbino

by Louise de la Ramée

Long ago in the city of Urbino there lived a master potter named Benedetto. Benedetto had a daughter, Pacifica, whom he loved very much. But the dearest thing in the world to him—dearer even then Pacifica—was his pottery, and his greatest sorrow was that he had no son to carry on his art. The sorrow was the greater because across the mountains a younger man was gaining fame as a potter, and in time seemed likely to outdo Benedetto and the pottery of Urbino.

Benedetto had a neighbor, and this neighbor had a son, a little fair-haired, grave-eyed child of seven, named Raphael. Raphael's father was an artist, and very early the child began to learn from him to hold the brush and mix colors. He was often seen, too, in the workshop of Benedetto, for the potter loved the boy, both for himself, and for the love that he already showed for art. For hours at a time Raphael would stand quietly beside the old man as he worked, noting each detail of the potter's skill, and storing up in his little head the things he learned there.

He was a friend, too, of the tall, dark-eyed Pacifica, who was ever ready to stop her work to play with him. But best of all, he loved big, gentle Luca. Luca had come down from the hills to learn the potter's trade from Benedetto. He was tall and straight, and he loved Benedetto's daughter with all his heart.

But, alas, poor Luca, good and handsome though he was, would never be an artist! He knew it. He knew also that

Benedetto would never look with favor upon any but a great artist as the husband of Pacifica, and he despaired of ever winning her. He often told his trouble to Raphael, who felt very sorry for the young man and comforted him as best he could.

One day Luca came to Raphael in deep trouble. An order had come from the duke for a great jar and platter. It was to be sent over the mountains as a gift to the duke's cousin. Everyone in the potter's workshop must strive to fill the order in a way that would be pleasing to the duke. Benedetto had let it be known that the man who was lucky enough to please the duke might become Benedetto's partner and likewise his son-in-law. Poor Luca was in despair. He knew very well that his chance of winning Pacifica was gone.

Raphael's tender heart was touched.

"How long do you have to complete this work, Luca?" he asked hopefully.

"Three months," answered Luca, "but it makes no difference. I could never do it in three years."

Raphael thought for a long while. At last, putting his hand in Luca's, he said, "Luca, let me try to paint a jar and platter."

If Luca had not been so miserable, the sight of the little fellow would have made him laugh.

"Please, Luca," pleaded the child. "I can paint, you know. I have often watched Benedetto at work. Please Luca, it can do no harm."

Finally, rather than hurt the boy's feelings, Luca assented.

---

favor: approval
despaired: lost all hope
assented: agreed

Day after day Raphael climbed the stairs to Luca's workroom. Pacifica, watching him, thought he went to watch and cheer Luca, and was sad because she knew that his faithfulness would do nothing toward helping Luca win the prize.

But up in the bare garret the child was working hard. How thankful he was for the hours spent with Benedetto, and for the lessons of his father, the painter. How anxiously he toiled, painting and rubbing out, and painting again. Not a word did he breathe about his work, nor would he even allow Luca to look at what he did. Each night he covered it carefully so that no one might catch a glimpse of it. Meanwhile Luca was working away hopelessly, too sad to notice his little friend.

At last, the day before the end of the three months, Raphael called Luca to see his work. Trembling with eagerness, he uncovered his jar and platter and showed them to his friend.

One glance was enough. The astonished youth fell on his knees, crying out in wonder at the beauty of the child's work.

Raphael danced up and down with joy.

"But, Raphael," cried poor Luca, "it can do me no good. This is your work. It would be cheating for me to win Pacifica this way. I could not do it."

"Wait," said the child. "I have a plan."

On the next day, the duke was to come to choose his pottery. From all the country round the youth had gathered, bringing their work to be judged. The pottery was placed on benches in the great workroom, each piece being marked with a number instead of a name, in order that the judges

---

garret: an attic room

might not know whose work it was, and that the judgment should be quite fair.

In the outer room Benedetto and a few friends waited for the duke to come. Little Raphael was there, very pale, clinging to his father's hand.

When the duke appeared, Benedetto led the way to his workroom. The duke passed along the row of jars and platters, praising each. At last, he stopped.

"This is beyond all comparison," he said turning to the potter. "Master Benedetto, whose work is this?"

Benedetto stepped forward and looked at the pottery. "It can be none of my people," he said. "I have no one in my workshop who could do work such as that. Number eleven," he added, looking at the gathering of potters, "step forward. The duke has chosen your work."

In the hush that followed, the child Raphael stepped out.

"I painted it," he said with a pleased smile. "I, Raphael."

Immediately the room was in confusion. The astonished potters gathered about the child, while Benedetto and Raphael's father looked on in amazement.

With tears in his eyes, the duke took a jewel that hung on a gold chain about his neck and placed it over Raphael's shoulders. "This is your first reward," he said. "You will have many, O wondrous child, who shall live when we are dust!"

Raphael kissed the duke's hand. Then he turned to his father. "Is it true," he asked, "that my jar and platter have been chosen?"

His father could only bow his head. "Then," said Raphael, looking up bravely at Benedetto, "Master, I claim the prize."

There was a little ripple of laughter.

Raphael Sanzio as a young man

"I am your pupil," said the child. "If you had not taught me your secrets, I could never have painted these. Now, dear Master, I give my right to my friend, Luca, who is the honestest man in all the world, and does love Pacifica as no other can do."

Benedetto burst into tears. "Indeed," he said, "I can refuse him nothing. He will give such glory to Urbino as the world has never seen."

And the words that Benedetto spoke were fulfilled in the years to come.

BEETHOVEN'S MOONLIGHT SONATA

It happened at Bonn. One moonlit winter's evening I called upon Beethoven, for I wanted him to take a walk, and afterward sup with me. In passing through some dark, narrow street, he paused suddenly. "Hush!" he said—"what sound is that? It is from my sonata in F!" he said eagerly. "Hark! How well it is played."

It was a little, run-down dwelling, and we paused outside and listened. The player went on, but in the midst of the finale there was a sudden break, then the voice of sobbing. "I cannot play anymore. It is so beautiful, it is utterly beyond my power to do it justice. Oh, what would I not give to go to the concert at Cologne!"

"Ah, my sister," said her companion, "why create regrets, when there is no remedy? We can scarcely pay our rent."

"You are right; and yet I wish for once in my life to hear some really wonderful music. But it is of no use."

Beethoven looked at me. "Let us go in," he said.

"Go in!" I exclaimed. "What can we go in for?"

"I will play for her," he said, in an excited tone. "Here is feeling—genius—understanding. I will play to her, and she will understand it." And, before I could prevent it, his hand was upon the door.

---

sonata: a musical piece, usually in three or four sections, for an
    instrument (such as the piano) or combination of instruments
    (such as piano and violin)
sup: to eat supper; to dine
finale: the closing section of a musical piece

A pale young man was sitting by the table, making shoes, and near him, leaning sorrowfully upon an old-fashioned fortepiano, sat a young girl, with a profusion of light hair falling over her face. Both were cleanly but very poorly dressed, and both started and turned toward us as we entered.

"Pardon me," said Beethoven, "but I heard music, and was tempted to enter. I am a musician."

The girl blushed, and the young man looked grave and somewhat annoyed.

"I—I also overheard something of what you said," continued my friend. "You wish to hear—that is, you would like—that is—Shall I play for you?"

There was something so odd in the whole affair, and something so comic and pleasant in the manner of the speaker, that the spell was broken in a moment, and all smiled involuntarily.

"Thank you!" said the shoemaker, "but our piano is so wretched, and we have no music."

"No music!" echoed my friend. "How, then, does the Fräulein—"

He paused, and then blushed deeply, for the girl looked full at him, and he saw that she was blind.

"I—I entreat your pardon!" he stammered. "But I had not perceived before. Then you play by ear?"

"Entirely."

---

fortepiano: an early kind of piano
profusion: a great quantity
started: moved in a quick, sudden way
involuntarily: not done on purpose
Fräulein: German for "Miss"
entreat: to plead; to request urgently
perceived: noticed

"And where do you hear the music, since you frequent no concerts?"

"I used to hear a lady practicing near us, when we lived at Brühl two years. During the summer evenings her windows were generally open, and I walked to and fro outside to listen to her."

She seemed shy; so Beethoven said no more, but seated himself quietly before the piano, and began to play. He had no sooner struck the first chord than I knew what would follow—how grand he would be that night. And I was not mistaken. Never, during all the years I knew him, did I hear him play as he then played to that blind girl and her brother. He was inspired. From the instant when his fingers began to wander along the keys, the very tone of the instrument began to grow sweeter and more equal.

The brother and sister were silent with wonder and rapture. The former laid aside his work; the latter, with her head bent slightly forward, and her hands pressed tightly over her breast, crouched down near the end of the piano, as if fearful lest even the beating of her heart should break the

---

frequent: to attend often
chord: three or more musical tones sounded at the same time
rapture: extreme happiness

flow of those magical, sweet sounds. It was as if we were all bound in a strange dream, and only feared to wake.

Suddenly the flame of the single candle wavered, sank, flickered, and went out. Beethoven paused, and I threw open the shutters, admitting a flood of brilliant moonlight. The room was almost as light as before, and the illumination fell strongest upon the piano and the player. But the chain of his ideas seemed to have been broken by the accident. His head dropped on his breast; his hands rested upon his knees; he seemed absorbed in meditation. It was thus for some time.

At length the young shoemaker rose, and approached him eagerly, yet reverently. "Wonderful man!" he said, in a low tone, "who and what are you?"

The composer smiled benevolently, indulgently, kindly. "Listen!" he said, and he played the opening bars of the sonata in F.

A cry of delight and recognition burst from them both, and exclaiming, "Then you are Beethoven!" they covered his hands with tears and kisses.

He rose to go, but we held him back with entreaties.

"Play to us once more—only once more!"

He suffered himself to be led back to the instrument. The moon shone brightly in through the window and lit up his glorious, rugged head and massive figure. "I will improvise a sonata to the moonlight!" Then, looking up thoughtfully to

wavered: shook slightly
meditation: deep thought
reverently: in a manner showing deep, awed respect
benevolently: kindly
indulgently: showing special favor
entreaties: requests
suffered: allowed
improvise: to make up; in music, to make up and perform a piece on the
    spot, without planning

the sky and stars, his hands dropped on the keys, and he began playing a sad and infinitely lovely movement, which crept gently over the instrument like the calm flow of moonlight over the dark earth.

This was followed by a wild, elfin passage in triple time— a sort of grotesque interlude, like the dance of sprites upon the sward. Then came a swift agitato finale—a breathless, hurrying, trembling movement, descriptive of flight and uncertainty, and vague terror, which carried us away on its rustling wings, and left us all in emotion and wonder.

"Farewell to you!" said Beethoven, pushing back his chair and turning toward the door— "farewell to you!"

"You will come again?" asked they, in one breath.

He paused and looked compassionately, almost tenderly, at the face of the blind girl. "Yes, yes," he said, hurriedly, "I will come again, and give the Fräulein some lessons. Farewell! I will soon come again!"

They followed us in silence more eloquent than words, and stood at their door till we were out of sight and hearing.

"Let us make haste back," said Beethoven, "that I may write out that sonata while I can yet remember it."

We did so, and he sat over it till long past dawn. And this was the origin of that "Moonlight Sonata" with which we are all so fondly acquainted.

---

infinitely: immeasurably
elfin: like an elf; magical
grotesque: bizarre; strange; out of proportion
interlude: a musical piece inserted between the parts of a longer
    composition
sprites: elf-like creatures
sward: grassy earth
agitato: an Italian term, used in music, meaning, "agitated, restless"
eloquent: expressive
make haste: an expression meaning "to hurry"

MARY CASSATT: ARTIST AND TRAILBLAZER

by Vanessa Wright

One day in Paris, in 1851, a seven-year-old American girl named Mary Cassatt went with her family to visit the Louvre, one of the world's greatest art museums. The little girl gazed up in wonder at paintings of the old masters, such as Leonardo da Vinci's *Mona Lisa*, Titian's mythical scenes, and Rembrandt's shadowy, brooding landscapes.

"Someday," she said to herself, "I will be as great an artist as they."

A few years later, young Mary Cassatt returned with her family to America. With the images she had seen in Paris still aglow in her mind, she wanted more than ever to become a professional artist. "In fact," she said to a friend, "I am going to paint better than the old masters!"

As soon as she was old enough, Cassatt entered the Pennsylvania Academy of Fine Arts. She took drawing classes, but was disappointed because the Academy's art collection had very few great paintings for her to study. At that time, not even the best American museums had collections that could compare with the great paintings hanging in the Louvre.

Cassatt remembered watching art students in Paris learn to paint by copying the great works in the Louvre. "If I want to be a serious painter," she thought, "it seems I must return to Europe."

---

brooding: gloomy

Cassatt's goal was clear, but there were many obstacles in her path. The year was 1865. Women did not have the right to vote. They were not allowed to attend the best art schools. In general, women were not expected or encouraged to become artists. And they were definitely not supposed to travel abroad alone. So when Cassatt told her father that she wished to study in Europe and become a professional artist, he strongly opposed her wishes.

But Cassatt persisted. She discussed, explained, and argued with her father until he changed his mind. Rather than resist her, he decided to support her artistic ambitions. And so in 1866, when Cassatt was twenty-two years old, she moved back to Paris, ready to fulfill her dreams.

In Paris, Cassatt studied with successful artists. She carefully copied paintings in the Louvre. She also packed up her brushes, rode out to the countryside, and painted the people and landscapes that caught her fancy.

Many people admired Cassatt's paintings of the French countryside. Her teachers admired them so much that they encouraged her to try to get them displayed in the great annual art exhibition called the Salon. At the Salon, some paintings were awarded ribbons or medals, but almost all artists whose work was chosen for the Salon would become successful. And, on the other side, it was almost impossible to succeed as a painter without exhibiting at the Salon.

It was not easy to get a painting picked for exhibition in the Salon. The jury that judged the paintings only liked a

---

abroad: outside one's home country
opposed: disagreed with
persisted: continued with determination
ambitions: goals; strong desires to achieve

certain kind of art. They chose paintings that resembled the work of the old masters: dark and serious, with smooth, blended colors. They wanted the subjects to be from history, mythology, or literature, arranged in formal poses, and painted to look perfect instead of like real people. They did not welcome originality.

The jury rejected the first painting Cassatt submitted for the Salon. But the next year, they accepted a painting, very much in the style of the old masters, showing a peasant woman sitting and holding a mandolin.

While it was a great honor to be chosen, Cassatt soon grew restless. She preferred to paint with bright colors and loose strokes. She liked painting ordinary people doing ordinary things. She was developing her own style, but it was not a style that the Salon's jury liked. "What should I do?" she wondered. "Should I paint to please the jurors of the Salon, or should I paint my own way?"

One day, as Cassatt walked past a gallery window, she saw a pastel drawing by a boldly original French artist, Edgar Degas. She stopped in front of the window and stared at it. She could not tear herself away. The next day she returned to look at Degas' work, and the next, and the next. "I used to go and flatten my nose against that window and absorb all I could of his art," she wrote to a friend. "It changed my life. I saw art then as I wanted to see it."

Some time later, Degas saw one of Cassatt's portraits. He noticed that while she painted with the skill and grace of the old masters, she also mixed in the ideas and techniques of newer artists. In her work, he recognized a kindred spirit. It

---

techniques: methods; ways of doing something
kindred spirit: someone who shares similar beliefs and values

is said that after he looked at her painting, he cried to his friend, "There is someone who feels as I do!"

Edgar Degas was one of the first artists known as the Impressionists, a group that also included Claude Monet and Auguste Renoir. The Impressionists were a group of experimental artists who tried to capture on canvas a brief but true impression of people, places, or objects. They abandoned the old masters' dark colors and smooth brushstrokes. Instead, they used bright, lively colors, and bold lines and brushstrokes. Instead of painting people in stiff, formal poses, they captured people in fleeting moments of everyday life. Degas, for example, painted ballet dancers in rehearsal or laundresses at work.

Degas saw hints of Impressionism in Cassatt's painting. So he hurried to her studio and invited her to exhibit with his group instead of with the Salon. For Cassatt, it meant giving up the success guaranteed by exhibiting with the Salon, but she accepted the offer. Later, she wrote to her friend, "At last I could work with complete independence without concerning myself with the eventual judgment of a jury. I hated conventional art. I began to live."

A year after she met Degas, Cassatt painted *A Little Girl in a Blue Armchair*. In the painting, a little girl sits sprawled in a big, comfy chair, with one hand casually reaching behind her head. A small dog sleeps on another chair nearby. The little girl does not look out from the painting. Her expression seems a little bored, as though she had just collapsed into the

---

experimental: trying new things
fleeting: passing quickly
laundresses: women who do other people's laundry for pay
conventional: ordinary; following accepted rules or practices
sprawled: spread out

chair and heaved a big sigh while wishing she had something else to do. The designs on the blue chairs are rendered with swift brushstrokes. Certainly, the Salon jury would not have approved of this painting!

As Cassatt experimented with the Impressionists' techniques, she began to develop her own individual style. For her subjects, she did not choose the usual landscapes or cityscapes. Instead, she often painted women going about their daily tasks, or mothers and their children sharing tender, trusting moments. Although Cassatt herself never had children, perhaps no artist has better captured the bond between mother and child.

Cassatt continued to try new techniques. After attending an exhibition of Japanese wood-block prints, she experimented with making her own prints and engravings.

Cassatt's A Little Girl in a Blue Armchair

rendered: made

Her friend Degas was greatly impressed, and thought her prints to be some of her best work.

Although Cassatt spent most of her life in Paris, she returned sometimes to the United States. She advised wealthy Americans who wished to buy and exhibit great European art, both the old masters as well as the best of the new paintings. More than any other person, Mary Cassatt helped introduce Americans to the work of the Impressionists. Some of the pieces Cassatt helped purchase still hang in American museums today.

Mary Cassatt was a trailblazer. Though women in her time had little freedom and few choices, she achieved her ambition to become a professional artist. She developed a style all her own, and chose the subjects that suited her, regardless of official opinions. She was the only American to exhibit with the Impressionists, and helped bridge the art gap between Europe and the United States.

"I have not done all I wanted to," she wrote before her death, "but I tried to make a good fight."

Mary Cassatt in 1914

---

trailblazer: one who does something new, who opens a new path for others to follow

YOUNG PABLO CASALS

by Mara Rockliff

Pablo Casals stood like a statue on the busy sidewalk.
People jostled past, shoving the slight young man from side
to side. Casals barely noticed. He was too busy soaking in the
sights and sounds of the great city.

A double-decker bus lumbered down the boulevard,
pulled by three giant horses. Carriages of all shapes and sizes
clattered over the worn stones. A fellow in a fashionable suit
whizzed past on one of those strange-looking contraptions
called "bicycles," almost causing a traffic pile-up.

Steam rose from the cart of a chestnut vendor. Casals
sniffed. Roasted chestnuts, yes—and another, less delicious,
odor, having to do with the many horses in the street.
But something else was in the air. Energy, perhaps.
Creativity. Success.

Ah, Paris!

Not only musicians like Casals, but every young artist
dreamed of Paris. Culturally, Paris at this time, at the dawn
of the twentieth century, was the center of the world. For
musicians, writers, painters, and artists of all kinds, all roads
seemed to lead to Paris.

As Casals daydreamed while standing on the busy
sidewalk, he imagined himself playing chess in a café with
the Impressionist painter Edgar Degas. Or sitting in a

---

jostled: pushed
lumbered: moved clumsily
contraptions: machines; gadgets
vendor: someone who sells something

darkened theater, feeling the sudden hush as the celebrated actress, Sarah Bernhardt, took the stage.

But his fondest dreams had to do with music, for music was life for this young cellist. Perhaps the brilliant French composer Maurice Ravel would create a piece inspired by Casals and his cello…

"Oof!"

A weight slammed into Casals, nearly knocking him off his feet. Startled, he looked up to see a broad mustachioed face glowering at him. Even if Casals could not understand all of the man's French words, he understood his vigorous gestures: it was time to move on.

As he hurried away, he felt his pocket. A reassuring crinkle told him that the letter from the Count of Morphy was still there. He patted it and smiled.

That letter was his ticket to success in Paris. That letter— and his own extraordinary musical talent, of course.

Casals thought of the last time he had come to Paris, in the fall of 1894. He was still a teenager then, eager to leave his home country of Spain and make his way as a musician in the larger world. His mother and two small brothers, Enrique and Luis, came too.

Casals' parents were devoted to his career. His father, a church organist, taught him music from a very early age. By the time he was four, he could already play piano, violin, and flute. At ten, he took up the cello, which proved to be the

celebrated: famous
fondest: most-loved
cellist: someone who plays the cello
glowering: staring angrily
vigorous: energetic, forceful

instrument he was destined to play as no one had ever played before. Soon, his parents realized that he was ready for more advanced training than his father could provide.

Señora de Casals took her eleven-year-old son from their village of Vendrell to the city of Barcelona and enrolled him in a music school. After three years, he played the cello better than his teacher. So she took him to Madrid to enter him at the conservatory. There he also met the Count of Morphy, a powerful nobleman who became his great friend.

After that, Casals and his mother moved on to France. With no means of support beyond the small sums that Señor de Casals was able to send, they found lodgings in the slums of Paris. Casals and his mother searched for work. His mother brought sewing home, but still they barely had enough to eat.

One day Casals met a violin student who told him of a job opening for a cellist. The job was in the orchestra of a second-rate music hall on the boulevard in Paris called the Champs-Élysées. The orchestra played popular music for traveling vaudeville acts and can-can dancers.

All those years studying at the music schools in Barcelona and Madrid, learning the glorious suites of Bach and the bold sonatas of Beethoven—all that training and practice, just to play dance-hall music? Casals needed the money. He took the job. Tram fare to the music hall was fifteen centimes, enough

---

Señora: Spanish for "Mrs."
conservatory: a school of music
slums: crowded areas of the city where the poor live
vaudeville acts: entertainment that includes skits, singers, dancers, acrobats, and comedians
can-can: a kind of dancing with very high kicks
suites: pieces of music that include dances
tram: a streetcar
centimes: small units of French money

to buy a bit of bread. So Casals made the long walk every day, round trip, carrying his cello. He was barely five feet tall. The cello was nearly his own size.

Winter came, and Paris turned bitterly cold. Casals became too sick to work. The family was left without the four francs a day that he'd been earning at the music hall. And now his mother needed to buy medicine as well as food.

One afternoon, Señora de Casals came home. From his bed, Casals stared at her in dismay. What had happened to her magnificent long black hair? It was ragged and short. His mother had sold her hair to a wigmaker for a few extra francs.

She laughed at his horror. "Never mind," she said. "Don't think about it. It is only hair, and hair grows back."

Soon, though, even she had to admit that Paris without enough food and heat was not a friendly place. The Casals family returned to Vendrell. There, in the Spanish warmth and sunlight, the young musician recovered.

More than four years had passed since then. Now, as Pablo Casals brushed himself off and walked down the busy streets of Paris, it was late 1899, and he was twenty-three years old. A new century was about to dawn. Surely, this time, Paris would open its arms to the charming little cellist who had already impressed the Queen of Spain.

Once more, Casals felt for his letter. This time he did not smile. Just a few weeks ago, the Count of Morphy, who had been ill for some time, had died. The Count had been like a second father to Casals. This letter of introduction to the great French conductor, Charles Lamoureux, was his last gift to his young friend.

---

francs: French money; 100 centimes = 1 franc
conductor: the leader of an orchestra

It was no small gift. Lamoureux's Sunday concerts were all the rage among Paris society. A chance to play with his orchestra could open the door to international success.

When he arrived, a boy showed Casals into the conductor's office. Lamoureux sat at a table, hunched over some papers. He was completely absorbed in his work. For several minutes, Casals waited quietly, but Lamoureux didn't even look up. The young man began to feel embarrassed.

At last he said, "I am sorry, sir, to intrude upon your work. I only wish to give you a letter from the Count de Morphy."

The conductor's head jerked up. From under his bushy eyebrows, he gave Casals a piercing glare. Why must he constantly be interrupted? Did people think his work was not important? Musicians came to him every day with letters praising their great talent. Was he expected to drop everything for some little Spanish cellist?

Casals answered simply, and with dignity, that the Count had trusted him to deliver his letter. Then he left.

He had reached the lobby when he heard footsteps pounding behind him. It was Lamoureux. Without a word, the conductor held out his hand. Casals gave him the letter, which he read.

Then he said, "Come tomorrow, young man, and bring your cello with you."

The next morning, Casals returned to the office. Again, the conductor was wrapped up in his work and ignored the young musician. Casals waited. Finally, Lamoureux snapped, "Play for me." Then he returned his attention to his work.

---

all the rage: an expression meaning "very popular"
dignity: nobility; self-respect

Casals began to play the cello part of a concerto. The first notes had hardly left his cello when Lamoureux put down his pen. A moment later, to the young man's astonishment, the conductor pushed himself to his feet. He stood leaning forward until Casals finished playing. Then he came forward and threw his arms around Casals. Tears glistened in the conductor's eyes.

"My dear boy," he said. "You will play in my first concert next month."

A few weeks later, Casals made his Paris debut with the Lamoureux orchestra—as a soloist. He played the same concerto he had played for the conductor in his office.

Casals was an overnight sensation. Invitations piled up to play at concerts and recitals across Paris. "Suddenly, all doors were open to me," he wrote years later. He would go on to worldwide fame and many years of musical accomplishment. Other cellists strove to copy his technique. Eventually, he became a conductor and led his own orchestra.

But he did not forget the family and friends who had helped make his success possible. "I had worked hard, it is true, but I had been greatly fortunate," he wrote. "Whatever I was, each of them was a part of me, and without any one of them I would have been that much less.... That is why gratitude and the knowledge of my debt have never left me."

concerto: a musical piece in which, usually, a soloist plays a main part accompanied by an orchestra
astonishment: great surprise
glistened: sparkled (usually said of something moist or wet)

MARIAN ANDERSON SINGS
by Mara Rockliff

The instant Marian Anderson stepped off the train in Washington, D.C., she found herself surrounded by reporters. Questions flew at her from every side.

The Daughters of the American Revolution have refused to let you sing at Constitution Hall because you are a Negro. How does that make you feel?

Are you insulted?

Are you angry?

What are you going to do?

For many of their questions, Anderson had no answer. But the answer to the last question was clear. She would do what she had always done, what she did best. She would sing.

Even as a little girl in Philadelphia, singing in her church choir, Marian Anderson knew her destiny lay in her rich, wide-ranging voice. But her father died when she was twelve. Her mother worked long hours cleaning houses and taking in laundry. She earned barely enough to feed and clothe her three daughters. Music lessons for young Marian seemed just a dream, but talent alone was not enough. She needed training.

A local music teacher generously offered Marian free lessons. But it was not long before the teacher said she'd taught her all she could. If Marian was really serious about her music, she should go to music school. Perhaps she could win a scholarship.

---

destiny: a person's fate in life

Marian Anderson rode the trolley downtown to the school. There she joined a long line of other excited applicants. Patiently, she waited for her turn. But when she reached the window, the clerk—a white girl her own age—looked right past her to the next person in line. She watched, bewildered, as the girl handed forms to everyone but her. Finally, she turned to Anderson and said, "What do you want?"

Anderson asked for an application form. The girl stared at her coldly. "We don't take colored," she said. Shocked and hurt, Anderson walked out.

At home, her mother urged her not to give up. If she was meant to sing, there would be a way. And there was. An Italian voice teacher who had trained many opera stars heard her sing and agreed to take her as his student. But his fees were more than she could possibly afford. Sadly, Anderson thanked him for his time and left.

However, her friends and neighbors were not about to let "our Marian" miss out on such an opportunity. They put on a benefit concert at the church and raised $600—enough for a whole year of voice lessons.

The work was hard. Marian sang splendidly without training, but she needed to learn to control her voice like a professional. She even needed to learn to breathe differently. She practiced her exercises over and over. And she learned new songs—Italian, German, French. At first, she simply memorized the words syllable by syllable. But how could she give true feeling to a song she didn't understand? So she had to study languages as well.

---

trolley: a streetcar
applicants: people who have applied for something

Those struggles were behind her now. Touring Europe, she'd become a huge sensation. Audiences crowded into concert halls to hear the elegant American contralto. With regal poise, she would stand by the piano, eyes closed, her velvety, expressive voice expanding to fill every corner of the room.

Once, after a concert, the legendary conductor Arturo Toscanini came backstage. "Yours is a voice," he told Anderson, "such as one hears once in a hundred years."

When she returned to the United States, fame and success followed. Here, too, she was invited to sing in the finest concert halls, often to sellout crowds. But across the footlights Anderson often saw only white faces. In many cities, in the South especially, people of her own race had to sit up in the balcony. And, as warmly as an audience applauded, after the show a restaurant or hotel manager might coldly turn her away.

Anderson responded to these slights with quiet dignity. She was determined not to let other people's fear and ignorance pull her away from what really mattered—her music.

The singer's popularity continued to grow. Her manager worked hard to find concert halls big enough to hold Anderson's growing audiences. When her tour schedule brought her to Washington, D.C., in 1939, the choice was obvious: the city's largest and grandest concert venue, Constitution Hall.

---

sensation: someone who causes great excitement
contralto: a female singer with a low voice
regal: royal; like a king or queen
poise: calm, confident self-assurance
ignorance: lack of knowledge
venue: the location where a special event or gathering occurs

Anderson's manager wrote to make arrangements. The date he wanted was already taken, he was told. He suggested other dates in April. He was told that those were taken, too. In fact, no dates were available at all.

Could this be true? Suspicious, the manager asked a well-known white pianist to try to book the hall. The answer came back: the pianist could have his pick of any date that spring.

The truth quickly came out. Constitution Hall was owned by the Daughters of the American Revolution. Only women—white women—whose ancestors had fought the British were allowed to join this group. And the DAR would not rent Constitution Hall to any African American performer, even one as widely admired as Marian Anderson.

News of this refusal outraged Anderson's many fans. Fellow musicians canceled their performances. Among them was the famous violinist, Jascha Heifetz, who said, "I am ashamed to play at Constitution Hall." Fiorello LaGuardia, the mayor of New York, sent the DAR a telegram: "No hall is too good for Marian Anderson." The First Lady, Eleanor Roosevelt, even resigned from the DAR in protest, making front-page headlines all over the country.

Everywhere Anderson went, reporters swarmed around, demanding a reaction. What could she say? The uproar saddened and embarrassed her. Dignified as always, she refused to speak out publicly against the DAR. Many of the group's members, she knew, disagreed with the national leadership. As she wrote later in her autobiography, she strongly believed that "a whole group should not be condemned because an individual or section of the group does a thing that is not right."

---

condemned: judged as wrong or evil

Anderson had faith that right would always win out in the end. All she wanted was to make beautiful music. She was certain she would find a place to sing.

Then came a surprising invitation—from the United States government. How would Anderson like to sing on Easter Sunday at the Lincoln Memorial? It would be an outdoor concert, free, open to all—and with no segregation.

Anderson struggled over her reply. She was a singer, not an activist. She did not enjoy being the center of attention for reasons other than her music. To sing at the Lincoln Memorial would be a bold political statement. At best, she'd feel uncomfortable. At worst, she might find herself at the center of an ugly riot.

"I studied my conscience," she wrote. "I could see that my significance as an individual was small in this affair. I had become, whether I liked it or not, a symbol, representing my people. I had to appear."

Easter Sunday arrived. Hours before the concert started, people began gathering at the Lincoln Memorial. By the time Anderson's car pulled up, the crowd had grown to 75,000. Millions more waited at home by their radios.

Police led Anderson through the throng to a platform in front of the monument. "My heart leaped wildly, and I could not talk," she wrote. "I even wondered whether I would be able to sing."

She barely noticed the many Washington notables who joined her on the platform. Members of President Roosevelt's cabinet, Supreme Court justices, senators, and congressmen were all on hand to hear the celebrated singer.

---

segregation: the separation of people based on their race
throng: a large crowd

Anderson looked out at the sea of faces, black and white, women, men, and children. "There seemed to be people as far as the eye could see," she wrote. "The crowd stretched in a great semicircle from the Lincoln Memorial around the reflecting pool on to the shaft of the Washington Monument. I had a feeling that a great wave of good will poured out from these people, almost engulfing me."

Standing tall and determined, Anderson looked like a queen. Inside, though, she was terrified.

The first notes of "The Star-Spangled Banner" boomed over the loudspeakers. For a desperate moment, Anderson felt as if she were choking. Would the words she knew so well refuse to come?

She found her voice. Thousands of voices joined Anderson's as she led her audience in the national anthem. She went on to sing "America," followed by an operatic aria, Schubert's "Ave Maria," and three traditional African American spirituals. Her voice soared, powerful, rich, and thrilling.

When she finished, a great roar went up. The crowd surged forward. They could not stop cheering and applauding.

Of all who gathered that day at the Lincoln Memorial, no one could have been moved more deeply than Marian Anderson. Her courage and faith had been rewarded. America had reached out to embrace one of its greatest singers.

"I am overwhelmed," Anderson told the crowd. "I can't tell you what you have done for me today. I thank you from the bottom of my heart again and again."

---

aria: in an opera, a melody sung by a single voice with orchestra
surged: moved with growing force, as a wave

FAVORITES
FROM FAMOUS BOOKS

THE JUNGLE BOOK

Now this is the Law of the Jungle—as old and as true as the sky;
And the Wolf that shall keep it may prosper, but the Wolf
that shall break it must die.
As the creeper that girdles the tree-trunk, the Law runneth
forward and back—
For the strength of the Pack is the Wolf, and the strength
of the Wolf is the Pack.

from
THE JUNGLE BOOK
by Rudyard Kipling

MOWGLI'S BROTHERS

Now Chil the Kite brings home the night
    That Mang the Bat sets free—
The herds are shut in byre and hut
    For loosed till dawn are we.
This is the hour of pride and power,
    Talon and tush and claw.
Oh, hear the call!—Good hunting all
    That keep the Jungle Law!

> —Night Song in the Jungle

It was seven o'clock of a very warm evening in the Seeonee hills when Father Wolf woke up from his day's rest, scratched himself, yawned, and spread out his paws one after the other to get rid of the sleepy feeling in their tips. Mother Wolf lay with her big gray nose dropped across her four tumbling, squealing cubs, and the moon shone into the mouth of the cave where they all lived. "*Augrh!*" said Father Wolf, "it is time to hunt again." And he was going to spring downhill when a little shadow with a bushy tail crossed the threshold and whined: "Good luck go with you, O Chief of the Wolves; and good luck and strong white teeth go with noble children, that they may never forget the hungry in this world."

---

kite: a bird of prey
byre: a cow barn
tush: a long, pointed tooth

It was the jackal—Tabaqui the Dish-licker—and the wolves of India despise Tabaqui because he runs about making mischief, and telling tales, and eating rags and pieces of leather from the village rubbish heaps. But they are afraid of him too, because Tabaqui, more than anyone else in the jungle, is apt to go mad, and then he forgets that he was ever afraid of anyone, and runs through the forest biting everything in his way. Even the tiger runs and hides when little Tabaqui goes mad, for madness is the most disgraceful thing that can overtake a wild creature. We call it hydrophobia, but they call it *dewanee*—the madness—and run.

"Enter, then, and look," said Father Wolf, stiffly, "but there is no food here."

"For a wolf, no," said Tabaqui, "but for so mean a person as myself a dry bone is a good feast. Who are we, the *Gidur-log* [the Jackal-People], to pick and choose?" He scuttled to the back of the cave, where he found the bone of a buck with some meat on it, and sat cracking the end merrily.

"All thanks for this good meal," he said, licking his lips. "How beautiful are the noble children! How large are their eyes! And so young too! Indeed, indeed, I might have remembered that the children of kings are men from the beginning."

---

hydrophobia: rabies
stiffly: proudly; formally
buck: a male deer

Now, Tabaqui knew as well as anyone else that there is nothing so unlucky as to compliment children to their faces; and it pleased him to see Mother and Father Wolf look uncomfortable.

Tabaqui sat still, rejoicing in the mischief that he had made, and then he said spitefully:

"Shere Khan, the Big One, has shifted his hunting grounds. He will hunt among these hills for the next moon, so he has told me."

Shere Khan was the tiger who lived near the Wainganga River, twenty miles away.

"He has no right!" Father Wolf began angrily. "By the Law of the Jungle he has no right to change his quarters without due warning. He will frighten every head of game within ten miles, and I—I have to kill for two, these days."

"His mother did not call him Lungri [the Lame One] for nothing," said Mother Wolf, quietly. "He has been lame in one foot from his birth. That is why he has only killed cattle. Now the villagers of the Wainganga are angry with him, and he has come here to make *our* villagers angry. They will scour the jungle for him when he is far away, and we and our children must run when the grass is set alight. Indeed, we are very grateful to Shere Khan!"

"Shall I tell him of your gratitude?" said Tabaqui.

"Out!" snapped Father Wolf. "Out and hunt with thy master. Thou hast done harm enough for one night."

"I go," said Tabaqui, quietly. "Ye can hear Shere Khan below in the thickets. I might have saved myself the message."

---

spitefully: in an intentionally mean and hurtful way
quarters: the place where one lives
scour: to search carefully

Father Wolf listened, and below in the valley that ran down to a little river, he heard the dry, angry, snarly, singsong whine of a tiger who has caught nothing and does not care if all the jungle knows it.

"The fool!" said Father Wolf. "To begin a night's work with that noise! Does he think that our buck are like his fat Wainganga bullocks?"

"*Hsh*. It is neither bullock nor buck he hunts tonight," said Mother Wolf. "It is Man."

The whine had changed to a sort of humming purr that seemed to come from every quarter of the compass. It was the noise that bewilders woodcutters and gypsies sleeping in the open, and makes them run sometimes into the very mouth of the tiger.

"Man!" said Father Wolf, showing all his white teeth. "*Faugh!* Are there not enough beetles and frogs in the tanks that he must eat Man, and on our ground too!"

The Law of the Jungle, which never orders anything without a reason, forbids every beast to eat Man except when he is killing to show his children how to kill, and then he must hunt outside the hunting grounds of his pack or tribe. The real reason for this is that man-killing means, sooner or later, the arrival of white men on elephants, with guns, and hundreds of brown men with gongs and rockets and torches. Then everybody in the jungle suffers. The reason the beasts give among themselves is that Man is the weakest and most defenseless of all living things, and it is unsportsmanlike to touch him. They say too—and it is true—that man-eaters become mangy, and lose their teeth.

The purr grew louder, and ended in the full-throated "*Aaarh!*" of the tiger's charge.

bullocks: young bulls

Then there was a howl—an untigerish howl—from Shere Khan. "He has missed," said Mother Wolf. "What is it?"

Father Wolf ran out a few paces and heard Shere Khan muttering and mumbling savagely, as he tumbled about in the scrub.

"The fool has had no more sense than to jump at a woodcutters' campfire, and has burned his feet," said Father Wolf with a grunt. "Tabaqui is with him."

"Something is coming uphill," said Mother Wolf, twitching one ear. "Get ready."

The bushes rustled a little in the thicket, and Father Wolf dropped with his haunches under him, ready for his leap. Then, if you had been watching, you would have seen the most wonderful thing in the world—the wolf checked in midspring. He made his bound before he saw what it was he was jumping at, and then he tried to stop himself. The result was that he shot up straight into the air for four or five feet, landing almost where he left ground.

"Man!" he snapped. "A man's cub. Look!"

Directly in front of him, holding on by a low branch, stood a naked brown baby who could just walk—as soft and as dimpled a little atom as ever came to a wolf's cave at night. He looked up into Father Wolf's face, and laughed.

"Is that a man's cub?" said Mother Wolf. "I have never seen one. Bring it here."

A wolf accustomed to moving his own cubs can, if necessary, mouth an egg without breaking it, and though Father Wolf's jaws closed right on the child's back, not a tooth even scratched the skin, as he laid it down among the cubs.

"How little! How naked, and—how bold!" said Mother Wolf softly. The baby was pushing his way between the cubs to get close to the warm hide. "*Ahai!* He is taking his meal with the others. And so this is a man's cub. Now, was there ever a wolf that could boast of a man's cub among her children?"

"I have heard now and again of such a thing, but never in our pack or in my time," said Father Wolf. "He is altogether without hair, and I could kill him with a touch of my foot. But see, he looks up and is not afraid."

The moonlight was blocked out of the mouth of the cave, for Shere Khan's great square head and shoulders were thrust into the entrance. Tabaqui, behind him, was squeaking: "My lord, my lord, it went in here!"

"Shere Khan does us great honor," said Father Wolf, but his eyes were very angry. "What does Shere Khan need?"

"My quarry. A man's cub went this way," said Shere Khan. "Its parents have run off. Give it to me."

Shere Khan had jumped at a woodcutters' campfire, as Father Wolf had said, and was furious from the pain of his burned feet. But Father Wolf knew that the mouth of the cave was too narrow for a tiger to come in by. Even where he was, Shere Khan's shoulders and forepaws were cramped for want of room, as a man's would be if he tried to fight in a barrel.

"The wolves are a free people," said Father Wolf. "They take orders from the head of the pack, and not from any striped cattle-killer. The man's cub is ours—to kill if we choose."

"Ye choose and ye do not choose! What talk is this of choosing? By the bull that I killed, am I to stand nosing into your dog's den for my fair dues? It is I, Shere Khan, who speak!"

---

quarry: prey; an animal hunted or chased

The tiger's roar filled the cave with thunder. Mother Wolf shook herself clear of the cubs and sprang forward, her eyes, like two green moons in the darkness, facing the blazing eyes of Shere Khan.

"And it is I, Raksha [The Demon], who answer. The man's cub is mine, Lungri—mine to me! He shall not be killed. He shall live to run with the pack and to hunt with the pack; and in the end, look you, hunter of little naked cubs—frog-eater—fish-killer—he shall hunt *thee*! Now get hence, or by the sambur that I killed (*I* eat no starved cattle), back thou goest to thy mother, burned beast of the jungle, lamer than ever thou camest into the world! Go!"

Father Wolf looked on amazed. He had almost forgotten the days when he won Mother Wolf in fair fight from five other wolves, when she ran in the pack and was not called the Demon for compliment's sake. Shere Khan might have faced Father Wolf, but he could not stand up against Mother Wolf, for he knew that where he was she had all the advantage of the ground, and would fight to the death. So he backed out of the cave mouth growling, and when he was clear he shouted:

"Each dog barks in his own yard! We will see what the pack will say to this fostering of man-cubs. The cub is mine, and to my teeth he will come in the end, O bush-tailed thieves!"

Mother Wolf threw herself down panting among the cubs, and Father Wolf said to her gravely:

"Shere Khan speaks this much truth. The cub must be shown to the pack. Wilt thou still keep him, Mother?"

get hence: go away
sambur: a large Asian deer (also spelled *sambar*)
fostering: the act of taking care of

"Keep him!" she gasped. "He came naked, by night, alone and very hungry; yet he was not afraid! Look, he has pushed one of my babes to one side already. And that lame butcher would have killed him and would have run off to the Wainganga while the villagers here hunted through all our lairs in revenge! Keep him? Assuredly I will keep him. Lie still, little frog. O thou Mowgli—for Mowgli the Frog I will call thee—the time will come when thou wilt hunt Shere Khan as he has hunted thee."

"But what will our pack say?" said Father Wolf.

The Law of the Jungle lays down very clearly that any wolf may, when he marries, withdraw from the pack he belongs to; but as soon as his cubs are old enough to stand on their feet he must bring them to the pack council, which is generally held once a month at full moon, in order that the other wolves may identify them. After that inspection the cubs are free to run where they please, and until they have killed their first buck no excuse is accepted if a grown wolf of the pack kills one of them. The punishment is death where the murderer can be found; and if you think for a minute you will see that this must be so.

Father Wolf waited till his cubs could run a little, and then on the night of the pack meeting took them and Mowgli and Mother Wolf to the Council Rock—a hilltop covered with stones and boulders where a hundred wolves could hide. Akela, the great gray Lone Wolf, who led all the pack by strength and cunning, lay out at full length on his rock, and below him sat forty or more wolves of every size and color, from badger-colored veterans who could handle a buck alone to young black three-year-olds who thought they could. The Lone Wolf had led them for a year now. He had fallen twice into a wolf trap in his youth, and once he had been beaten and left for dead; so he knew the manners and customs of men. There was very little talking at the rock. The cubs tumbled over each other in the center of the circle where their mothers and fathers sat, and now and again a senior wolf would go quietly up to a cub, look at him carefully, and return to his place on noiseless feet. Sometimes a mother would push her cub far out into the moonlight, to be sure that he had not been overlooked. Akela from his rock would cry: "Ye know the Law—ye know the Law. Look well, O wolves!" And the anxious mothers would take up the call: "Look—look well, O wolves!"

At last—and Mother Wolf's neck bristles lifted as the time came—Father Wolf pushed "Mowgli the Frog," as they called him, into the center, where he sat laughing and playing with some pebbles that glistened in the moonlight.

Akela never raised his head from his paws, but went on with the monotonous cry: "Look well!" A muffled roar came up from behind the rocks—the voice of Shere Khan crying: "The cub is mine. Give him to me. What have the Free People to do with a man's cub?"

Akela never even twitched his ears. All he said was: "Look well, O wolves! What have the Free People to do with the orders of any save the Free People? Look well!"

There was a chorus of deep growls, and a young wolf in his fourth year flung back Shere Khan's question to Akela: "What have the Free People to do with a man's cub?" Now the Law of the Jungle lays down that if there is any dispute as to the right of a cub to be accepted by the pack, he must be spoken for by at least two members of the pack who are not his father and mother.

"Who speaks for this cub?" said Akela. "Among the Free People who speaks?" There was no answer, and Mother Wolf got ready for what she knew would be her last fight, if things came to fighting.

Then the only other creature who is allowed at the pack council—Baloo, the sleepy brown bear who teaches the wolf cubs the Law of the Jungle: old Baloo, who can come and go where he pleases because he eats only nuts and roots and honey—rose upon his hind quarters and grunted.

"The man's cub—the man's cub?" he said. "*I* speak for the man's cub. There is no harm in a man's cub. I have no gift of words, but I speak the truth. Let him run with the pack, and be entered with the others. I myself will teach him."

"We need yet another," said Akela. "Baloo has spoken, and he is our teacher for the young cubs. Who speaks besides Baloo?"

A black shadow dropped down into the circle. It was Bagheera the Black Panther, inky black all over, but with the panther markings showing up in certain lights like the pattern of watered silk. Everybody knew Bagheera, and nobody cared to cross his path, for he was as cunning as Tabaqui, as bold as the wild buffalo, and as reckless as the wounded elephant. But he had a voice as soft as wild honey dripping from a tree, and a skin softer than down.

"O Akela, and ye the Free People," he purred, "I have no right in your assembly, but the Law of the Jungle says that if there is a doubt which is not a killing matter in regard to a new cub, the life of that cub may be bought at a price. And the Law does not say who may or may not pay that price. Am I right?"

"Good! Good!" said the young wolves, who are always hungry. "Listen to Bagheera. The cub can be bought for a price. It is the Law."

"Knowing that I have no right to speak here, I ask your leave."

"Speak then," cried twenty voices.

"To kill a naked cub is shame. Besides, he may make better sport for you when he is grown. Baloo has spoken in his behalf. Now to Baloo's word I will add one bull, and a fat one, newly killed, not half a mile from here, if ye will accept the man's cub according to the Law. Is it difficult?"

There was a clamor of scores of voices, saying: "What matter? He will die in the winter rains. He will scorch in the sun. What harm can a naked frog do us? Let him run with the pack. Where is the bull, Bagheera? Let him be accepted." And then came Akela's deep bay, crying: "Look well—look well, O wolves!"

Mowgli was still deeply interested in the pebbles, and he did not notice when the wolves came and looked at him one by one. At last they all went down the hill for the dead bull, and only Akela, Bagheera, Baloo, and Mowgli's own wolves were left. Shere Khan roared still in the night, for he was very angry that Mowgli had not been handed over to him.

"Ay, roar well," said Bagheera, under his whiskers, "for the time comes when this naked thing will make thee roar to another tune, or I know nothing of man."

"It was well done," said Akela. "Men and their cubs are very wise. He may be a help in time."

"Truly, a help in time of need, for none can hope to lead the pack forever," said Bagheera.

Akela said nothing. He was thinking of the time that comes to every leader of every pack when his strength goes from him and he gets feebler and feebler, till at last he is killed by the wolves and a new leader comes up—to be killed in his turn.

"Take him away," he said to Father Wolf, "and train him as befits one of the Free People."

And that is how Mowgli was entered into the Seeonee Wolf Pack for the price of a bull and on Baloo's good word.

---

scores: many (one score = twenty)

Now you must be content to skip ten or eleven whole years, and only guess at all the wonderful life that Mowgli led among the wolves, because if it were written out it would fill ever so many books. He grew up with the cubs, though they, of course, were grown wolves almost before he was a child, and Father Wolf taught him his business, and the meaning of things in the jungle, till every rustle in the grass, every breath of the warm night air, every note of the owls above his head, every scratch of a bat's claws as it roosted for a while in a tree, and every splash of every little fish jumping in a pool, meant just as much to him as the work of his office means to a business man. When he was not learning he sat out in the sun and slept, and ate and went to sleep again; when he felt dirty or hot he swam in the forest pools; and when he wanted honey (Baloo told him that honey and nuts were just as pleasant to eat as raw meat) he climbed up for it, and that Bagheera showed him how to do. Bagheera would lie out on a branch and call: "Come along, Little Brother," and at first Mowgli would cling like the sloth, but afterward he would fling himself through the branches almost as boldly as the gray ape. He took his place at the Council Rock, too, when the pack met, and there he discovered that if he stared hard at any wolf, the wolf would be forced to drop his eyes, and so he used to stare for fun. At other times he would pick the long thorns out of the pads of his friends, for wolves suffer terribly from thorns and burs in their coats. He would go down the hillside into the cultivated lands by night, and look very curiously at the villagers in their huts, but he had a mistrust of men because Bagheera showed him a square box with a drop-gate so cunningly hidden in the jungle that he

---

sloth: an animal of the tropical forests that hangs from trees by its claws
cultivated: farmed

nearly walked into it, and told him that it was a trap. He loved better than anything else to go with Bagheera into the dark warm heart of the forest, to sleep all through the drowsy day, and at night see how Bagheera did his killing. Bagheera killed right and left as he felt hungry, and so did Mowgli—with one exception. As soon as he was old enough to understand things, Bagheera told him that he must never touch cattle because he had been bought into the pack at the price of a bull's life. "All the jungle is thine," said Bagheera, "and thou canst kill everything that thou art strong enough to kill; but for the sake of the bull that bought thee thou must never kill or eat any cattle young or old. That is the Law of the Jungle." Mowgli obeyed faithfully.

And he grew and grew strong as a boy must grow who does not know that he is learning any lessons, and who has nothing in the world to think of except things to eat.

Mother Wolf told him once or twice that Shere Khan was not a creature to be trusted, and that someday he must kill Shere Khan. But though a young wolf would have remembered that advice every hour, Mowgli forgot it because he was only a boy—though he would have called himself a wolf if he had been able to speak in any human tongue.

Shere Khan was always crossing his path in the jungle, for as Akela grew older and feebler the lame tiger had come to be great friends with the younger wolves of the pack, who followed him for scraps, a thing Akela would never have allowed if he had dared to push his authority to the proper bounds. Then Shere Khan would flatter them and wonder that such fine young hunters were content to be led by a dying wolf and a man's cub. "They tell me," Shere Khan would say, "that at council ye dare not look him between the eyes." And the young wolves would growl and bristle.

Bagheera, who had eyes and ears everywhere, knew something of this, and once or twice he told Mowgli in so many words that Shere Khan would kill him someday. And Mowgli would laugh and answer: "I have the pack and I have thee; and Baloo, though he is so lazy, might strike a blow or two for my sake. Why should I be afraid?"

It was one very warm day that a new notion came to Bagheera— born of something that he had heard. Perhaps Sahi the Porcupine had told him; but he said to Mowgli when they were deep in the jungle, as the boy lay with his head on Bagheera's beautiful black skin: "Little Brother, how often have I told thee that Shere Khan is thy enemy?"

"As many times as there are nuts on that palm," said Mowgli, who, naturally, could not count. "What of it? I am sleepy, Bagheera, and Shere Khan is all long tail and loud talk—like Mor, the Peacock."

"But this is no time for sleeping. Baloo knows it; I know it; the pack knows it; and even the foolish, foolish deer know. Tabaqui has told thee, too."

"Ho! Ho!" said Mowgli. "Tabaqui came to me not long ago with some rude talk that I was a naked man's cub and not fit to dig pignuts; but I caught Tabaqui by the tail and swung him twice against a palm tree to teach him better manners."

"That was foolishness, for though Tabaqui is a mischief maker, he would have told thee of something that concerned thee closely. Open those eyes, Little Brother. Shere Khan dare not kill thee in the jungle; but remember, Akela is very old, and soon the day comes when he cannot kill his buck, and then he will be leader no more. Many of the wolves that

---

notion: an idea

looked thee over when thou wast brought to the council first are old too, and the young wolves believe, as Shere Khan has taught them, that a man-cub has no place with the pack. In a little time thou wilt be a man."

"And what is a man that he should not run with his brothers?" said Mowgli. "I was born in the jungle. I have obeyed the Law of the Jungle, and there is no wolf of ours from whose paws I have not pulled a thorn. Surely they are my brothers!"

Bagheera stretched himself at full length and half shut his eyes. "Little Brother," said he, "feel under my jaw."

Mowgli put up his strong brown hand, and just under Bagheera's silky chin, where the giant rolling muscles were all hid by the glossy hair, he came upon a little bald spot.

"There is no one in the jungle that knows that I, Bagheera, carry that mark—the mark of the collar. And yet, Little Brother, I was born among men, and it was among men that my mother died—in the cages of the king's palace at Oodeypore. It was because of this that I paid the price for thee at the council when thou wast a little naked cub. Yes, I too was born among men. I had never seen the jungle. They fed me behind bars from an iron pan till one night I felt that I was Bagheera—the Panther—and no man's plaything, and I broke the silly lock with one blow of my paw and came away. And because I had learned the ways of men, I became more terrible in the jungle than Shere Khan. Is it not so?"

"Yes," said Mowgli, "all the jungle fears Bagheera—all except Mowgli."

"Oh, *thou* art a man's cub," said the black panther, very tenderly, "and even as I returned to my jungle, so thou must

go back to men at last—to the men who are thy brothers—if thou art not killed in the council."

"But why—but why should any wish to kill me?" said Mowgli.

"Look at me," said Bagheera, and Mowgli looked at him steadily between the eyes. The big panther turned his head away in half a minute.

"*That* is why," he said, shifting his paw on the leaves. "Not even I can look thee between the eyes, and I was born among men, and I love thee, Little Brother. The others they hate thee because their eyes cannot meet thine; because thou art wise; because thou hast pulled out thorns from their feet—because thou art a man."

"I did not know these things," said Mowgli, sullenly, and he frowned under his heavy black eyebrows.

"What is the Law of the Jungle? Strike first and then give tongue. By thy very carelessness they know that thou art a man. But be wise. It is in my heart that when Akela misses his next kill—and at each hunt it costs him more to pin the buck—the pack will turn against him and against thee. They will hold a jungle council at the rock, and then—and then—I have it!" said Bagheera, leaping up. "Go thou down quickly to the men's huts in the valley, and take some of the Red Flower which they grow there, so that when the time comes thou mayest have even a stronger friend than I or Baloo or those of the pack that love thee. Get the Red Flower."

By Red Flower Bagheera meant fire, only no creature in the jungle will call fire by its proper name. Every beast lives in deadly fear of it, and invents a hundred ways of describing it.

"The Red Flower?" said Mowgli. "That grows outside their huts in the twilight. I will get some."

"There speaks the man's cub," said Bagheera, proudly. "Remember that it grows in little pots. Get one swiftly, and keep it by thee for time of need."

"Good!" said Mowgli. "I go. But art thou sure, O my Bagheera"—he slipped his arm round the splendid neck and looked deep into the big eyes—"art thou sure that all this is Shere Khan's doing?"

"By the broken lock that freed me, I am sure, Little Brother."

"Then, by the bull that bought me, I will pay Shere Khan full tale for this, and it may be a little over," said Mowgli, and he bounded away.

---

tale: total; amount

"That is a man. That is all a man," said Bagheera to himself, lying down again. "Oh, Shere Khan, never was a blacker hunting than that frog hunt of thine ten years ago!"

Mowgli was far and far through the forest, running hard, and his heart was hot in him. He came to the cave as the evening mist rose, and drew breath, and looked down the valley. The cubs were out, but Mother Wolf, at the back of the cave, knew by his breathing that something was troubling her frog.

"What is it, son?" she said.

"Some bat's chatter of Shere Khan," he called back. "I hunt among the plowed fields tonight." And he plunged downward through the bushes, to the stream at the bottom of the valley. There he checked, for he heard the yell of the pack hunting, heard the bellow of a hunted sambur, and the snort as the buck turned at bay. Then there were wicked, bitter howls from the young wolves: "Akela! Akela! Let the Lone Wolf show his strength. Room for the leader of the pack! Spring, Akela!"

The Lone Wolf must have sprung and missed his hold, for Mowgli heard the snap of his teeth and then a yelp as the sambur knocked him over with his forefoot.

He did not wait for anything more, but dashed on; and the yells grew fainter behind him as he ran into the croplands where the villagers lived.

"Bagheera spoke truth," he panted, as he nestled down in some cattle fodder by the window of a hut. "Tomorrow is one day both for Akela and for me."

Then he pressed his face close to the window and watched the fire on the hearth. He saw the husbandman's wife get up

---

fodder: food for cattle, horses, sheep; hay
husbandman: farmer

and feed it in the night with black lumps; and when the morning came and the mists were all white and cold, he saw the man's child pick up a wicker pot plastered inside with earth, fill it with lumps of red-hot charcoal, put it under his blanket, and go out to tend the cows in the byre.

"Is that all?" said Mowgli. "If a cub can do it, there is nothing to fear." So he strode round the corner and met the boy, took the pot from his hand, and disappeared into the mist while the boy howled with fear.

"They are very like me," said Mowgli, blowing into the pot as he had seen the woman do. "This thing will die if I do not give it things to eat." And he dropped twigs and dried bark on the red stuff. Halfway up the hill he met Bagheera with the morning dew shining like moonstones on his coat.

"Akela has missed," said the panther. "They would have killed him last night, but they needed thee also. They were looking for thee on the hill."

"I was among the plowed lands. I am ready. See!" Mowgli held up the fire-pot.

"Good! Now, I have seen men thrust a dry branch into that stuff, and presently the Red Flower blossomed at the end of it. Art thou not afraid?"

"No. Why should I fear? I remember now—if it is not a dream—how, before I was a wolf, I lay beside the Red Flower, and it was warm and pleasant."

All that day Mowgli sat in the cave tending his fire-pot and dipping dry branches into it to see how they looked. He found a branch that satisfied him, and in the evening when Tabaqui came to the cave and told him rudely enough that he was wanted at the Council Rock, he laughed till Tabaqui ran away. Then Mowgli went to the council, still laughing.

presently: soon

Akela the Lone Wolf lay by the side of his rock as a sign that the leadership of the pack was open, and Shere Khan with his following of scrap-fed wolves walked to and fro openly being flattered. Bagheera lay close to Mowgli, and the fire-pot was between Mowgli's knees. When they were all gathered together, Shere Khan began to speak—a thing he would never have dared to do when Akela was in his prime.

"He has no right," whispered Bagheera. "Say so. He is a dog's son. He will be frightened."

Mowgli sprang to his feet. "Free People," he cried, "does Shere Khan lead the pack? What has a tiger to do with our leadership?"

"Seeing that the leadership is yet open, and being asked to speak—" Shere Khan began.

"By whom?" said Mowgli. "Are we all jackals, to fawn on this cattle-butcher? The leadership of the pack is with the pack alone."

There were yells of "Silence, thou man's cub!" "Let him speak. He has kept our Law." And at last the seniors of the Pack thundered: "Let the Dead Wolf speak." When a leader of the pack has missed his kill, he is called the Dead Wolf as long as he lives, which is not long.

Akela raised his old head wearily:

"Free People, and ye too, jackals of Shere Khan, for twelve seasons I have led ye to and from the kill, and in all that time not one has been trapped or maimed. Now I have missed my kill. Ye know how that plot was made. Ye know how ye brought me up to an untried buck to make my weakness known. It was cleverly done. Your right is to kill me here on the Council Rock, now. Therefore, I ask, who comes to make an end of the Lone Wolf? For it is my right, by the Law of the Jungle, that ye come one by one."

There was a long hush, for no single wolf cared to fight Akela to the death. Then Shere Khan roared: *"Bah!* What have we to do with this toothless fool? He is doomed to die! It is the man-cub who has lived too long. Free People, he was my meat from the first. Give him to me. I am weary of this man-wolf folly. He has troubled the jungle for ten seasons. Give me the man-cub, or I will hunt here always, and not give you one bone. He is a man, a man's child, and from the marrow of my bones I hate him!"

Then more than half the pack yelled: "A man! A man! What has a man to do with us? Let him go to his own place."

"And turn all the people of the villages against us?" clamored Shere Khan. "No! Give him to me. He is a man, and none of us can look him between the eyes."

Akela lifted his head again, and said: "He has eaten our food. He has slept with us. He has driven game for us. He has broken no word of the Law of the Jungle."

"Also, I paid for him with a bull when he was accepted. The worth of a bull is little, but Bagheera's honor is something that he will perhaps fight for," said Bagheera in his gentlest voice.

"A bull paid ten years ago!" the pack snarled. "What do we care for bones ten years old?"

"Or for a pledge?" said Bagheera, his white teeth bared under his lip. "Well are ye called the Free People!"

"No man's cub can run with the People of the Jungle," howled Shere Khan. "Give him to me!"

"He is our brother in all but blood," Akela went on, "and ye would kill him here! In truth, I have lived too long. Some of ye are eaters of cattle, and of others I have heard that, under Shere Khan's teaching, ye go by dark night and snatch

pledge: a promise

children from the villager's doorstep. Therefore I know ye to be cowards, and it is to cowards I speak. It is certain that I must die, and my life is of no worth, or I would offer that in the man-cub's place. But for the sake of the honor of the pack—a little matter that by being without a leader ye have forgotten—I promise that if ye let the man-cub go to his own place, I will not, when my time comes to die, bare one tooth against ye. I will die without fighting. That will at least save the pack three lives. More I cannot do; but if ye will, I can save ye the shame that comes of killing a brother against whom there is no fault—a brother spoken for and bought into the pack according to the Law of the Jungle."

"He is a man—a man—a man!" snarled the Pack. And most of the wolves began to gather round Shere Khan, whose tail was beginning to switch.

"Now the business is in thy hands," said Bagheera to Mowgli. "*We* can do no more except fight."

Mowgli stood upright—the fire-pot in his hands. Then he stretched out his arms, and yawned in the face of the council. But he was furious with rage and sorrow, for, wolflike, the wolves had never told him how they hated him. "Listen you!" he cried. "There is no need for this dog's jabber. Ye have told me so often tonight that I am a man (and indeed I would have been a wolf with you to my life's end) that I feel your words are true. So I do not call ye my brothers any more, but *sag* [dogs], as a man should. What ye will do, and what ye will not do, is not yours to say. That matter is with *me*. And that we may see the matter more plainly, I, the man, have brought here a little of the Red Flower which ye, dogs, fear."

---

jabber: nonsense; chatter

He flung the fire-pot on the ground, and some of the red coals lit a tuft of dried moss that flared up, as all the council drew back in terror before the leaping flames.

Mowgli thrust his dead branch into the fire till the twigs lit and crackled, and whirled it above his head among the cowering wolves.

"Thou art the master," said Bagheera in an undertone. "Save Akela from the death. He was ever thy friend."

Akela, the grim old wolf who had never asked for mercy in his life, gave one piteous look at Mowgli as the boy stood all naked, his long black hair tossing over his shoulders in the light of the blazing branch that made the shadows jump and quiver.

"Good!" said Mowgli, staring round slowly. "I see that ye are dogs. I go from you to my own people—if they be my own people. The jungle is shut to me, and I must forget your talk and your companionship; but I will be more merciful than ye are. Because I was all but your brother in blood, I promise that when I am a man among men I will not betray ye to men as ye have betrayed me." He kicked the fire with his foot, and the sparks flew up. "There shall be no war between any of us in the pack. But here is a debt to pay before I go." He strode forward to where Shere Khan sat blinking stupidly at the flames, and caught him by the tuft on his chin. Bagheera followed in case of accidents. "Up, dog!" Mowgli cried. "Up, when a man speaks, or I will set that coat ablaze!"

Shere Khan's ears lay flat back on his head, and he shut his eyes, for the blazing branch was very near.

---

cowering: shrinking back in fear
undertone: a low or soft voice

"This cattle-killer said he would kill me in the council because he had not killed me when I was a cub. Thus and thus, then, do we beat dogs when we are men. Stir a whisker, Lungri, and I ram the Red Flower down thy gullet!" He beat Shere Khan over the head with the branch, and the tiger whimpered and whined in an agony of fear.

"*Pah!* Singed jungle cat—go now! But remember when next I come to the Council Rock, as a man should come, it will be with Shere Khan's hide on my head. For the rest, Akela goes free to live as he pleases. Ye will *not* kill him, because that is not my will. Nor do I think that ye will sit here any longer, lolling out your tongues as though ye were somebodies, instead of dogs whom I drive out—thus! Go!" The fire was burning furiously at the end of the branch, and Mowgli struck right and left round the circle, and the wolves ran howling with the sparks burning their fur. At last there were only Akela, Bagheera, and perhaps ten wolves that had taken Mowgli's part. Then something began to hurt Mowgli inside him, as he had never been hurt in his life before, and he caught his breath and sobbed, and the tears ran down his face.

"What is it? What is it?" he said. "I do not wish to leave the jungle, and I do not know what this is. Am I dying, Bagheera?"

"No, Little Brother. That is only tears such as men use," said Bagheera. "Now I know thou art a man, and a man's cub no longer. The jungle is shut indeed to thee henceforward. Let them fall, Mowgli. They are only tears." So Mowgli sat and cried as though his heart would break; and he had never cried in all his life before.

---

gullet: throat
henceforward: from this time on

"Now," he said, "I will go to men. But first I must say farewell to my mother." And he went to the cave where she lived with Father Wolf, and he cried on her coat, while the four cubs howled miserably.

"Ye will not forget me?" said Mowgli.

"Never while we can follow a trail," said the cubs. "Come to the foot of the hill when thou art a man, and we will talk to thee; and we will come into the croplands to play with thee by night."

"Come soon!" said Father Wolf. "Oh, wise little frog, come again soon, for we be old, thy mother and I."

"Come soon," said Mother Wolf, "little naked son of mine, for, listen, child of man, I loved thee more than ever I loved my cubs."

"I will surely come," said Mowgli, "and when I come it will be to lay out Shere Khan's hide upon the Council Rock. Do not forget me! Tell them in the jungle never to forget me!"

The dawn was beginning to break when Mowgli went down the hillside alone, to meet those mysterious things that are called men.

HUNTING SONG OF THE SEEONEE PACK

As the dawn was breaking the sambur belled
    Once, twice, and again!
And a doe leaped up and a doe leaped up
From the pond in the wood where the wild deer sup.
This I, scouting alone, beheld
    Once, twice, and again!

---

belled: bellowed; cried out

As the dawn was breaking the sambur belled
    Once, twice, and again!
And a wolf stole back and a wolf stole back
To carry the word to the waiting pack,
And we sought and we found and we bayed on his track
    Once, twice, and again!

As the dawn was breaking the wolf pack yelled
    Once, twice, and again!
Feet in the jungle that leave no mark!
Eyes that can see in the dark—the dark!
Tongue—give tongue to it! Hark! O hark!
    Once, twice, and again!

give tongue: an expression meaning "speak it, say it aloud"

"TIGER — TIGER!"

What of the hunting, hunter bold?
  Brother, the watch was long and cold.
What of the quarry ye went to kill?
  Brother, he crops in the jungle still.
Where is the power that made your pride?
  Brother, it ebbs from my flank and side.
Where is the haste that ye hurry by?
  Brother, I go to my lair to die.

When Mowgli left the wolf's cave after the fight with the pack at the Council Rock, he went down to the plowed lands where the villagers lived, but he would not stop there because it was too near to the jungle, and he knew that he had made at least one bad enemy at the council. So he hurried on, keeping to the rough road that ran down the valley, and followed it at a steady jog-trot for nearly twenty miles, till he came to a country that he did not know. The valley opened out into a great plain dotted over with rocks and cut up with ravines. At one end stood a little village, and at the other the thick jungle came down in a sweep to the grazing grounds, and stopped there as though it had been cut off with a hoe. All over the plain, cattle and buffaloes were grazing, and when the little boys in charge of the herds saw Mowgli they shouted and ran away, and

---

crops: grazes; eats
ebbs: flows away; lessens
ravines: small, narrow valleys with steep sides

the yellow pariah dogs that hang about every Indian village barked. Mowgli walked on, for he was feeling hungry, and when he came to the village gate he saw the big thornbush that was drawn up before the gate at twilight pushed to one side.

"*Umph!*" he said, for he had come across more than one such barricade in his night rambles after things to eat. "So men are afraid of the people of the jungle here also." He sat down by the gate, and when a man came out he stood up, opened his mouth, and pointed down it to show that he wanted food. The man stared, and ran back up the one street of the village shouting for the priest, who was a big, fat man dressed in white, with a red and yellow mark on his forehead. The priest came to the gate, and with him at least a hundred people, who stared and talked and shouted and pointed at Mowgli.

"They have no manners, these Men-Folk," said Mowgli to himself. "Only the gray ape would behave as they do." So he threw back his long hair and frowned at the crowd.

"What is there to be afraid of?" said the priest. "Look at the marks on his arms and legs. They are the bites of wolves. He is but a wolf-child run away from the jungle."

Of course, in playing together, the cubs had often nipped Mowgli harder than they intended, and there were white scars all over his arms and legs. But he would have been the last person in the world to call these bites, for he knew what real biting meant.

"*Arré! Arré!*" said two or three women together. "To be bitten by wolves, poor child! He is a handsome boy. He has

---

pariah: outcast
barricade: a barrier
rambles: wanderings

eyes like red fire. By my honor, Messua, he is not unlike thy
boy that was taken by the tiger."

"Let me look," said a woman with heavy copper rings on
her wrists and ankles, and she peered at Mowgli under the
palm of her hand. "Indeed he is not. He is thinner, but he has
the very look of my boy."

The priest was a clever man, and he knew that Messua
was wife to the richest villager in the place. So he looked up
at the sky for a minute, and said solemnly: "What the jungle

solemnly: in a holy and serious way

has taken the jungle has restored. Take the boy into thy house, my sister, and forget not to honor the priest who sees so far into the lives of men."

"By the bull that bought me," said Mowgli to himself, "but all this talking is like another looking-over by the pack! Well, if I am a man, a man I must become."

The crowd parted as the woman beckoned Mowgli to her hut, where there was a red lacquered bedstead, a great earthen grain chest with funny raised patterns on it, half a dozen copper cooking pots, an image of a Hindu god in a little alcove, and on the wall a real looking glass, such as they sell at the country fairs for eight cents.

She gave him a long drink of milk and some bread, and then she laid her hand on his head and looked into his eyes, for she thought perhaps that he might be her real son come back from the jungle where the tiger had taken him. So she said: "Nathoo, O Nathoo!" Mowgli did not show that he knew the name. "Dost thou not remember the day when I gave thee thy new shoes?" She touched his foot, and it was almost as hard as horn. "No," she said, sorrowfully, "those feet have never worn shoes, but thou art very like my Nathoo, and thou shalt be my son."

Mowgli was uneasy, because he had never been under a roof before; but as he looked at the thatch, he saw that he could tear it out any time if he wanted to get away, and that the window had no fastenings. "What is the good of a man," he said to himself at last, "if he does not understand man's talk? Now I am as silly and dumb as a man would be with us in the jungle. I must speak their talk."

---

restored: given back
lacquered: having a glossy finish
alcove: a small space carved into a wall

He had not learned while he was with the wolves to imitate the challenge of bucks in the jungle and the grunt of the little wild pig for fun. So, as soon as Messua pronounced a word Mowgli would imitate it almost perfectly, and before dark he had learned the names of many things in the hut.

There was a difficulty at bedtime, because Mowgli would not sleep under anything that looked so like a panther trap as that hut, and when they shut the door he went through the window. "Give him his will," said Messua's husband. "Remember he can never till now have slept on a bed. If he is indeed sent in the place of our son he will not run away."

So Mowgli stretched himself in some long clean grass at the edge of the field, but before he had closed his eyes a soft gray nose poked him under the chin.

"Phew!" said Gray Brother (he was the eldest of Mother Wolf's cubs). "This is a poor reward for following thee twenty miles. Thou smellest of wood smoke and cattle—altogether like a man already. Wake, Little Brother; I bring news."

"Are all well in the jungle?" said Mowgli, hugging him.

"All except the wolves that were burned with the Red Flower. Now, listen. Shere Khan has gone away to hunt far off till his coat grows again, for he is badly singed. When he returns he swears that he will lay thy bones in the Wainganga."

"There are two words to that. I also have made a little promise. But news is always good. I am tired tonight—very tired with new things, Gray Brother—but bring me the news always."

"Thou wilt not forget that thou art a wolf? Men will not make thee forget?" said Gray Brother, anxiously.

anxiously: with great worry

"Never. I will always remember that I love thee and all in our cave, but also I will always remember that I have been cast out of the pack."

"And that thou mayest be cast out of another pack. Men are only men, Little Brother, and their talk is like the talk of frogs in a pond. When I come down here again, I will wait for thee in the bamboos at the edge of the grazing ground."

For three months after that night Mowgli hardly ever left the village gate, he was so busy learning the ways and customs of men. First he had to wear a cloth round him, which annoyed him horribly; and then he had to learn about money, which he did not in the least understand, and about plowing, of which he did not see the use. Then the little children in the village made him very angry. Luckily, the Law of the Jungle had taught him to keep his temper, for in the jungle, life and food depend on keeping your temper; but when they made fun of him because he would not play games or fly kites, or because he mispronounced some word, only the knowledge that it was unsportsmanlike to kill little naked cubs kept him from picking them up and breaking them in two. He did not know his own strength in the least. In the jungle he knew he was weak compared with the beasts, but in the village people said that he was as strong as a bull. He certainly had no notion of what fear was, for when the village priest told him that the god in the temple would be angry with him if he ate the priest's mangoes, he picked up the image, brought it over to the priest's house, and asked the priest to make the god angry and he would be happy to fight him. It was a horrible scandal, but the priest hushed it up, and Messua's husband paid much good silver to comfort the god.

And Mowgli had not the faintest idea of the difference that caste makes between man and man. When the potter's donkey slipped in the clay pit, Mowgli hauled it out by the tail, and helped to stack the pots for their journey to the market at Khanhiwara. That was very shocking, too, for the potter is a low-caste man, and his donkey is worse. When the priest scolded him, Mowgli threatened to put him on the donkey, too, and the priest told Messua's husband that Mowgli had better be set to work as soon as possible; and the village headman told Mowgli that he would have to go out with the buffaloes next day, and herd them while they grazed. No one was more pleased than Mowgli; and that night, because he had been appointed a servant of the village, as it were, he went off to a circle that met every evening on a masonry platform under a great fig tree. It was the village club, and the headman and the watchman and the barber, who knew all the gossip of the village, and old Buldeo, the village hunter, who had a Tower musket, met and smoked. The monkeys sat and talked in the upper branches, and there was a hole under the platform where a cobra lived, and he had his little platter of milk every night because he was sacred; and the old men sat around the tree and talked, and pulled at the big *huqas* (the water-pipes) till far into the night. They told wonderful tales of gods and men and ghosts; and Buldeo told even more wonderful ones of the ways of beasts in the jungle, till the eyes of the children sitting outside the circle bulged out of their heads. Most of the tales were about animals, for the jungle was always at their door. The deer and the wild pig grubbed up their crops,

---

caste: at one time, in Hinduism, a social class one was born into
masonry: made of stones or bricks
grubbed: dug up

and now and again the tiger carried off a man at twilight, within sight of the village gates.

Mowgli, who naturally knew something about what they were talking of, had to cover his face not to show that he was laughing, while Buldeo, the Tower musket across his knees, climbed on from one wonderful story to another, and Mowgli's shoulders shook.

Buldeo was explaining how the tiger that had carried away Messua's son was a ghost-tiger, and his body was inhabited by the ghost of a wicked, old moneylender, who had died some years ago. "And I know that this is true," he said, "because Purun Dass always limped from the blow that he got in a riot when his account books were burned, and the tiger that I speak of *he* limps, too, for the tracks of his pads are unequal."

"True, true, that must be the truth," said the graybeards nodding together.

"Are all these tales such cobwebs and moon-talk?" said Mowgli. "That tiger limps because he was born lame, as everyone knows. To talk of the soul of a moneylender in a beast that never had the courage of a jackal is child's talk."

Buldeo was speechless with surprise for a moment, and the headman stared.

"Oho! It is the jungle brat, is it?" said Buldeo. "If thou art so wise, better bring his hide to Khanhiwara, for the Government has set a hundred rupees on his life. Better still, talk not when thy elders speak."

Mowgli rose to go. "All the evening I have lain here listening," he called back over his shoulder, "and, except once or twice, Buldeo has not said one word of truth concerning the jungle, which is at his very doors. How then shall I believe the tales of ghosts, and gods, and goblins which he says he has seen?"

"It is full time that boy went to herding," said the headman, while Buldeo puffed and snorted at Mowgli's impertinence.

The custom of most Indian villages is for a few boys to take the cattle and buffaloes out to graze in the early morning, and bring them back at night; and the very cattle that would trample a white man to death allow themselves to be banged and bullied and shouted at by children that hardly come up to their noses. So long as the boys keep with the herds they are safe, for not even the tiger will charge a mob of cattle. But if they straggle to pick flowers or hunt lizards, they are sometimes carried off. Mowgli went through the village street in the dawn, sitting on the back of Rama, the great herd bull; and the slaty-blue buffaloes, with their long, backward sweeping horns and savage eyes, rose out their byres, one by one, and followed him, and Mowgli made it very clear to the children with him that he was the master. He beat the buffaloes with a long, polished bamboo, and told Kamya, one of the boys, to graze the cattle by themselves, while he went on with the buffaloes, and to be very careful not to stray away from the herd.

An Indian grazing ground is all rocks, and scrub, and tussocks, and little ravines, among which the herds scatter and disappear. The buffaloes generally keep to the pools and muddy places, where they lie wallowing or basking in the warm mud for hours. Mowgli drove them on to the edge of the plain where the Wainganga came out of the jungle; then

impertinence: rudeness; disrespect
tussocks: tufts

he dropped from Rama's neck, trotted off to a bamboo clump, and found Gray Brother. "Ah," said Gray Brother, "I have waited here very many days. What is the meaning of this cattle-herding work?"

"It is an order," said Mowgli. "I am a village herd for a while. What news of Shere Khan?"

"He has come back to this country, and has waited here a long time for thee. Now he has gone off again, for the game is scarce. But he means to kill thee."

"Very good," said Mowgli. "So long as he is away do thou or one of the four brothers sit on that rock, so that I can see thee as I come out of the village. When he comes back wait for me in the ravine by the *dhâk* tree in the center of the plain. We need not walk into Shere Khan's mouth."

Then Mowgli picked out a shady place, and lay down and slept while the buffaloes grazed round him. Herding in India is one of the laziest things in the world. The cattle move and crunch, and lie down, and move on again, and they do not even low. They only grunt, and the buffaloes very seldom say anything, but get down into the muddy pools one after another, and work their way into the mud till only their noses and staring china-blue eyes show above the surface, and then they lie like logs. The sun makes the rocks dance in the heat, and the herd-children hear one kite (never any more) whistling almost out of sight overhead, and they know that if they died, or a cow died, that kite would sweep down, and the next kite miles away would see him drop and follow, and the next, and the next, and almost before they were dead there would be a score of hungry kites come out

scarce: hard to find; very little
low: to moo

of nowhere. Then they sleep and wake and sleep again, and weave little baskets of dried grass and put grasshoppers in them, or catch two praying mantises and make them fight; or string a necklace of red and black jungle nuts, or watch a lizard basking on a rock, or a snake hunting a frog near the wallows. Then they sing long, long songs with odd native quavers at the end of them, and the day seems longer than most people's whole lives, and perhaps they make a mud castle with mud figures of men and horses and buffaloes, and put reeds into the men's hands, and pretend that they are kings and the figures are their armies, or that they are gods to be worshiped. Then evening comes and the children call, and the buffaloes lumber up out of the sticky mud with noises like gunshots going off one after the other, and they all string across the gray plain back to the twinkling village lights.

Day after day Mowgli would lead the buffaloes out to their wallows, and day after day he would see Gray Brother's back a mile and a half away across the plain (so he knew that Shere Khan had not come back), and day after day he would lie on the grass listening to the noises round him, and dreaming of old days in the jungle. If Shere Khan had made a false step with his lame paw up in the jungles by the Wainganga, Mowgli would have heard him in those long, still mornings.

At last a day came when he did not see Gray Brother at the signal place, and he laughed and headed the buffaloes for the ravine by the *dhâk* tree, which was all covered with golden-red flowers. There sat Gray Brother, every bristle on his back lifted.

---

wallows: muddy areas

"He has hidden for a month to throw thee off thy guard. He crossed the ranges last night with Tabaqui, hotfoot on thy trail," said the wolf, panting.

Mowgli frowned. "I am not afraid of Shere Khan, but Tabaqui is very cunning."

"Have no fear," said Gray Brother, licking his lips a little. "I met Tabaqui in the dawn. Now he is telling all his wisdom to the kites, but he told me everything before I broke his back. Shere Khan's plan is to wait for thee at the village gate this evening—for thee and for no one else. He is lying up now, in the big dry ravine of the Wainganga."

"Has he eaten today, or does he hunt empty?" said Mowgli, for the answer meant life and death to him.

"He killed at dawn—a pig—and he has drunk too. Remember, Shere Khan could never fast, even for the sake of revenge."

"Oh! Fool, fool! What a cub's cub it is! Eaten and drunk too, and he thinks that I shall wait till he has slept! Now, where does he lie up? If there were but ten of us we might pull him down as he lies. These buffaloes will not charge unless they wind him, and I cannot speak their language. Can we get behind his track so that they may smell it?"

"He swam far down the Wainganga to cut that off," said Gray Brother.

"Tabaqui told him that, I know. He would never have thought of it alone." Mowgli stood with his finger in his mouth, thinking. "The big ravine of the Wainganga. That opens out on the plain not half a mile from here. I can take the herd round through the jungle to the head of the ravine and then sweep down—but he would slink out at the foot. We must block that end. Gray Brother, canst thou cut the herd in two for me?"

"Not I, perhaps—but I have brought a wise helper." Gray Brother trotted off and dropped into a hole. Then there lifted up a huge gray head that Mowgli knew well, and the hot air was filled with the most desolate cry of all the jungle—the hunting howl of a wolf at midday.

"Akela! Akela!" said Mowgli, clapping his hands. "I might have known that thou wouldst not forget me. We have a big work in hand. Cut the herd in two, Akela. Keep the cows and calves together, and the bulls and the plow buffaloes by themselves."

The two wolves ran, ladies'-chain fashion, in and out of the herd, which snorted and threw up its head, and separated into two clumps. In one, the cow buffaloes stood with their calves in the center, and glared and pawed, ready, if a wolf would only stay still, to charge down and trample the life out of him. In the other, the bulls and the young bulls snorted and stamped, but though they looked more imposing they were much less dangerous, for they had no calves to protect. No six men could have divided the herd so neatly.

"What orders!" panted Akela. "They are trying to join again."

Mowgli slipped on to Rama's back. "Drive the bulls away to the left, Akela. Gray Brother, when we are gone, hold the cows together, and drive them into the foot of the ravine."

"How far?" said Gray Brother, panting and snapping.

"Till the sides are higher than Shere Khan can jump," shouted Mowgli. "Keep them there till we come down." The bulls swept off as Akela bayed, and Gray Brother stopped in front of the cows. They charged down on him, and he ran

---

desolate: sorrowful; terribly sad
imposing: impressive in size or bearing

just before them to the foot of the ravine, as Akela drove the bulls far to the left.

"Well done! Another charge and they are fairly started. Careful, now—careful, Akela. A snap too much and the bulls will charge. *Hujah!* This is wilder work than driving black-buck. Didst thou think these creatures could move so swiftly?" Mowgli called.

"I have—have hunted these too in my time," gasped Akela in the dust. "Shall I turn them into the jungle?"

"Aye! Turn. Swiftly turn them! Rama is mad with rage. Oh, if I could only tell him what I need of him today."

The bulls were turned, to the right this time, and crashed into the standing thicket. The other herd-children, watching with the cattle half a mile away, hurried to the village as fast as their legs could carry them, crying that the buffaloes had gone mad and run away. But Mowgli's plan was simple enough. All he wanted to do was to make a big circle uphill and get at the head of the ravine, and then take the bulls down it and catch Shere Khan between the bulls and the cows, for he knew that after a meal and a full drink Shere Khan would not be in any condition to fight or to clamber up the sides of the ravine. He was soothing the buffaloes now by voice, and Akela had dropped far to the rear, only whimpering once or twice to hurry the rear guard. It was a long, long circle, for they did not wish to get too near the ravine and give Shere Khan warning. At last Mowgli rounded up the bewildered herd at the head of the ravine on a grassy patch that sloped steeply down to the ravine itself. From that height you could see across the tops of the trees down to the plain below; but what Mowgli looked at was the sides of the ravine, and he saw with a great deal of

---

bewildered: completely confused

satisfaction that they ran nearly straight up and down, while the vines and creepers that hung over them would give no foothold to a tiger who wanted to get out.

"Let them breathe, Akela," he said, holding up his hand. "They have not winded him yet. Let them breathe. I must tell Shere Khan who comes. We have him in the trap."

He put his hands to his mouth and shouted down the ravine—it was almost like shouting down a tunnel—and the echoes jumped from rock to rock.

After a long time there came back the drawling, sleepy snarl of a full-fed tiger just wakened.

"Who calls?" said Shere Khan, and a splendid peacock fluttered up out of the ravine screeching.

"I, Mowgli. Cattle thief, it is time to come to the Council Rock! Down—hurry them down, Akela! Down, Rama, down!"

The herd paused for an instant at the edge of the slope, but Akela gave tongue in the full hunting-yell, and they pitched over one after the other just as steamers shoot rapids, the sand and stones spurting up round them. Once started, there was no chance of stopping, and before they were fairly in the bed of the ravine Rama winded Shere Khan and bellowed.

"Ha! Ha!" said Mowgli, on his back. "Now thou knowest!" And the torrent of black horns, foaming muzzles, and staring eyes whirled down the ravine just as boulders go down in flood time, the weaker buffaloes being shouldered out to the sides of the ravine where they tore through the creepers. They knew what the business was before them—the terrible charge of the buffalo herd against which no tiger can hope to stand. Shere Khan heard the thunder of their hoofs, picked himself up, and lumbered down the ravine, looking

torrent: a violent flood

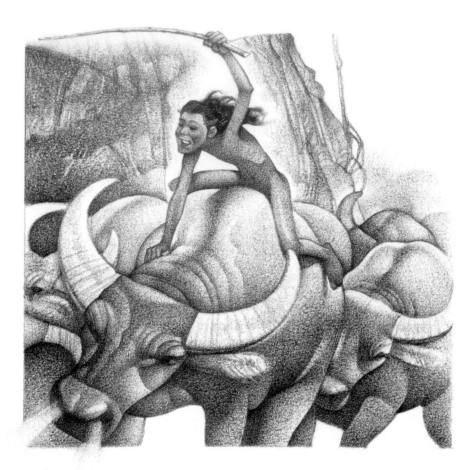

from side to side for some way of escape, but the walls of the
ravine were straight and he had to hold on, heavy with his
dinner and his drink, willing to do anything rather than
fight. The herd splashed through the pool he had just left,
bellowing till the narrow cut rang. Mowgli heard an
answering bellow from the foot of the ravine, saw Shere
Khan turn (the tiger knew if the worst came to the worst it
was better to meet the bulls than the cows with their calves),
and then Rama tripped, stumbled, and went on again over
something soft, and, with the bulls at his heels, crashed full
into the other herd, while the weaker buffaloes were lifted
clean off their feet by the shock of the meeting. That charge

carried both herds out into the plain, goring and stamping and snorting. Mowgli watched his time, and slipped off Rama's neck, laying about him right and left with his stick.

"Quick, Akela! Break them up. Scatter them, or they will be fighting one another. Drive them away, Akela. *Hai*, Rama! *Hai! Hai! Hai*, my children. Softly now, softly! It is all over."

Akela and Gray Brother ran to and fro nipping the buffaloes' legs, and though the herd wheeled once to charge up the ravine again, Mowgli managed to turn Rama, and the others followed him to the wallows.

Shere Khan needed no more trampling. He was dead, and the kites were coming for him already.

"Brothers, that was a dog's death," said Mowgli, feeling for the knife he always carried in a sheath round his neck now that he lived with men. "But he would never have shown fight. *Wallah!* His hide will look well on the Council Rock. We must get to work swiftly."

A boy trained among men would never have dreamed of skinning a ten-foot tiger alone, but Mowgli knew better than anyone else how an animal's skin is fitted on, and how it can be taken off. But it was hard work, and Mowgli slashed and tore and grunted for an hour, while the wolves lolled out their tongues, or came forward and tugged as he ordered them. Presently a hand fell on his shoulder, and looking up he saw Buldeo with the Tower musket. The children had told the village about the buffalo stampede, and Buldeo went out angrily, only too anxious to correct Mowgli for not taking better care of the herd. The wolves dropped out of sight as soon as they saw the man coming.

"What is this folly?" said Buldeo, angrily. "To think that thou canst skin a tiger! Where did the buffaloes kill him? It is the Lame Tiger, too, and there is a hundred rupees on his head. Well, well, we will overlook thy letting the herd run off, and perhaps I will give thee one of the rupees of the reward when I have taken the skin to Khanhiwara." He fumbled in his waist-cloth for flint and steel, and stooped down to singe Shere Khan's whiskers. Most native hunters always singe a tiger's whiskers to prevent his ghost from haunting them.

"Hum!" said Mowgli, half to himself as he ripped back the skin of a forepaw. "So thou wilt take the hide to Khanhiwara for the reward, and perhaps give me one rupee? Now it is in my mind that I need the skin for my own use. Heh! Old man, take away that fire!"

"What talk is this to the chief hunter of the village? Thy luck and the stupidity of thy buffaloes have helped thee to this kill. The tiger has just fed, or he would have gone twenty miles by this time. Thou canst not even skin him properly, little beggar brat, and forsooth I, Buldeo, must be told not to singe his whiskers. Mowgli, I will not give thee one anna of the reward, but only a very big beating. Leave the carcass!"

"By the bull that bought me," said Mowgli, who was trying to get at the shoulder, "must I stay babbling to an old ape all noon? Here, Akela, this man plagues me."

Buldeo, who was still stooping over Shere Khan's head, found himself sprawling on the grass, with a gray wolf standing over him, while Mowgli went on skinning as though he were alone in all India.

"Ye-es," he said, between his teeth. "Thou art altogether right, Buldeo. Thou wilt never give me one anna of the reward. There is an old war between this lame tiger and myself—a very old war, and—I have won."

---

carcass: the dead body of an animal
plagues: annoys constantly

To do Buldeo justice, if he had been ten years younger he would have taken his chance with Akela had he met the wolf in the woods, but a wolf who obeyed the orders of this boy who had private wars with man-eating tigers was not a common animal. It was sorcery, magic of the worst kind, thought Buldeo, and he wondered whether the amulet round his neck would protect him. He lay as still as still, expecting every minute to see Mowgli turn into a tiger too.

"Maharaj! Great King," he said at last, in a husky whisper.

"Yes," said Mowgli, without turning his head, chuckling a little.

"I am an old man. I did not know that thou wast anything more than a herdsboy. May I rise up and go away, or will thy servant tear me to pieces?"

"Go, and peace go with thee. Only, another time do not meddle with my game. Let him go, Akela."

Buldeo hobbled away to the village as fast as he could, looking back over his shoulder in case Mowgli should change into something terrible. When he got to the village he told a tale of magic and enchantment and sorcery that made the priest look very grave.

Mowgli went on with his work, but it was nearly twilight before he and the wolves had drawn the great gay skin clear of the body.

"Now we must hide this and take the buffaloes home! Help me to herd them, Akela."

The herd rounded up in the misty twilight, and when they got near the village Mowgli saw lights, and heard the conches and bells in the temple blowing and banging. Half the village seemed to be waiting for him by the gate. "That is

conches: shells that, when blown, make a loud trumpeting noise because I have killed Shere Khan," he said to himself. But a shower of stones whistled about his ears, and the villagers shouted: "Sorcerer! Wolf's brat! Jungle-demon! Go away! Get hence quickly, or the priest will turn thee into a wolf again. Shoot, Buldeo, shoot!"

The old Tower musket went off with a bang, and a young buffalo bellowed in pain.

"More sorcery!" shouted the villagers. "He can turn bullets. Buldeo, that was thy buffalo."

"Now what is this?" said Mowgli, bewildered, as the stones flew thicker.

"They are not unlike the pack, these brothers of thine," said Akela, sitting down composedly. "It is in my head that, if bullets mean anything, they would cast thee out."

"Wolf! Wolf's cub! Go away!" shouted the priest, waving a sprig of the sacred *tulsi* plant.

"Again? Last time it was because I was a man. This time it is because I am a wolf. Let us go, Akela."

A woman—it was Messua—ran across to the herd, and cried: "Oh, my son, my son! They say thou art a sorcerer who can turn himself into a beast at will. I do not believe, but go away or they will kill thee. Buldeo says thou art a wizard, but I know thou hast avenged Nathoo's death."

"Come back, Messua!" shouted the crowd. "Come back, or we will stone thee."

Mowgli laughed a little short ugly laugh, for a stone had hit him in the mouth. "Run back, Messua. This is one of the foolish tales they tell under the big tree at dusk. I have at least paid for thy son's life. Farewell, and run quickly, for I

---

avenged: taken revenge for; gotten even

shall send the herd in more swiftly than their brickbats. I am no wizard, Messua. Farewell!"

"Now, once more, Akela," he cried. "Bring the herd in."

The buffaloes were anxious enough to get to the village. They hardly needed Akela's yell, but charged through the gate like a whirlwind, scattering the crowd right and left.

"Keep count!" shouted Mowgli scornfully. "It may be that I have stolen one of them. Keep count, for I will do your herding no more. Fare you well, children of men, and thank Messua that I do not come in with my wolves and hunt you up and down your street."

He turned on his heel and walked away with the Lone Wolf, and as he looked up at the stars he felt happy. "No more sleeping in traps for me, Akela. Let us get Shere Khan's skin and go away. No, we will not hurt the village, for Messua was kind to me."

When the moon rose over the plain, making it look all milky, the horrified villagers saw Mowgli, with two wolves at his heels and a bundle on his head, trotting across at the steady wolf's trot that eats up the long miles like fire. Then they banged the temple bells and blew the conches louder than ever. And Messua cried, and Buldeo embroidered the story of his adventures in the jungle, till he ended by saying that Akela stood up on his hind legs and talked like a man.

The moon was just going down when Mowgli and the two wolves came to the hill of the Council Rock, and they stopped at Mother Wolf's cave.

"They have cast me out from the man pack, Mother," shouted Mowgli, "but I come with the hide of Shere Khan to

brickbats: fragments of stones or other hard materials
embroidered: added false or exaggerated details

keep my word." Mother Wolf walked stiffly from the cave with the cubs behind her, and her eyes glowed as she saw the skin.

"I told him on that day, when he crammed his head and shoulders into this cave, hunting for thy life, little frog—I told him that the hunter would be the hunted. It is well done."

"Little Brother, it is well done," said a deep voice in the thicket. "We were lonely in the jungle without thee," and Bagheera came running to Mowgli's bare feet. They clambered up the Council Rock together, and Mowgli spread the skin out on the flat stone where Akela used to sit, and pegged it down with four slivers of bamboo, and Akela lay down upon it, and called the old call to the council: "Look, look well, O wolves," exactly as he had called when Mowgli was first brought there.

Ever since Akela had been deposed, the pack had been without a leader, hunting and fighting at their own pleasure. But they answered the call from habit, and some of them were lame from the traps they had fallen into, and some limped from shot wounds, and some were mangy from eating bad food, and many were missing. But they came to the Council Rock, all that were left of them, and saw Shere Khan's striped hide on the rock, and the huge claws dangling at the end of the empty dangling feet.

"Look well, O wolves. Have I kept my word?" said Mowgli. And the wolves bayed Yes, and one tattered wolf howled:

"Lead us again, O Akela. Lead us again, O man-cub, for we be sick of this lawlessness, and we would be the Free People once more."

"Nay," purred Bagheera, "that may not be. When ye are full-fed, the madness may come upon you again. Not for nothing are ye called the Free People. Ye fought for freedom, and it is yours. Eat it, O wolves."

"Man pack and wolf pack have cast me out," said Mowgli. "Now I will hunt alone in the jungle."

"And we will hunt with thee," said the four cubs.

So Mowgli went away and hunted with the four cubs in the jungle from that day on. But he was not always alone, because, years afterward, he became a man and married.

But that is a story for grown-ups.

MOWGLI'S SONG
That He Sang At The Coucncil Rock
When He Danced On Shere Khan's Hide

The Song of Mowgli—I, Mowgli, am singing. Let the jungle
  listen to the things I have done.

Shere Khan said he would kill—would kill! At the gates in the
  twilight he would kill Mowgli the Frog!

He ate and he drank. Drink deep, Shere Khan, for when wilt thou
  drink again? Sleep and dream of the kill.

I am alone on the grazing grounds. Gray Brother, come to me!
  Come to me, Lone Wolf, for there is big game afoot!

Bring up the great bull buffaloes, the blue-skinned herd bulls
  with the angry eyes. Drive them to and fro as I order.

Sleepest thou still, Shere Khan? Wake, O wake! Here come I,
  and the bulls are behind.

Rama the king of the buffaloes stamped with his foot. Waters of
  the Wainganga, whither went Shere Khan?

He is not Sahi to dig holes, nor Mor the Peacock that he should
  fly. He is not Mang the Bat to hang in the branches. Little
  bamboos that creak together, tell me where he ran?

Ow! He is there. *Ahoo!* He is there. Under the feet of Rama lies the
  Lame One! Up, Shere Khan! Up and kill! Here is meat;
  break the necks of the bulls!

Hsh! He is asleep. We will not wake him, for his strength is very
  great. The kites have come down to see it. The black ants have
  come up to know it. There is a great assembly in his honor.

---

afoot: moving on foot
whither: to what place

Alala! I have no cloth to wrap me. The kites will see that I am
naked. I am ashamed to meet all these people.

Lend me thy coat, Shere Khan. Lend me thy gay striped coat that I
  may go to the Council Rock.

By the bull that bought me I made a promise—a little promise.
  Only thy coat is lacking before I keep my word.

With the knife, with the knife that men use, with the knife of the
  hunter, I will stoop down for my gift.

Waters of the Wainganga, Shere Khan gives me his coat for the love
  that he bears me. Pull, Gray Brother! Pull, Akela! Heavy is
  the hide of Shere Khan.

The man pack are angry. They throw stones and talk child's talk.
  My mouth is bleeding. Let me run away.

Through the night, through the hot night, run swiftly with me, my
  brothers. We will leave the lights of the village and go to the
  low moon.

Waters of the Wainganga the man pack have cast me out. I did
  them no harm, but they were afraid of me. Why?

Wolf pack, ye have cast me out too. The jungle is shut to me and
  the village gates are shut. Why?

As Mang flies between the beasts and birds, so fly I between the
  village and the jungle. Why?

I dance on the hide of Shere Khan, but my heart is very heavy.

My mouth is cut and wounded with the stones from the village, but
my heart is very light, because I have come back to the jungle.
Why?

These two things fight together in me as the snakes fight in the
spring. The water comes out of my eyes, yet I laugh while it
falls. Why?

I am two Mowglis, but the hide of Shere Khan is under my feet.

All the jungle knows that I have killed Shere Khan. Look, look well
O wolves!

Ahae! My heart is heavy with the things that I do not understand.

THE TYGER
by William Blake

Tyger! Tyger! burning bright
   In the forests of the night,
   What immortal hand or eye
   Could frame thy fearful symmetry?

In what distant deeps or skies
   Burnt the fire of thine eyes?
   On what wings dare he aspire?
   What the hand dare seize the fire?

And what shoulder, and what art,
   Could twist the sinews of thy heart?
   And when thy heart began to beat,
   What dread hand? and what dread feet?

What the hammer? what the chain?
   In what furnace was thy brain?
   What the anvil? what dread grasp
   Dare its deadly terrors clasp?

---

immortal: free from death; never dying
frame: to create
symmetry: balanced form
deeps: seas
aspire: to try with great hope
art: skill
sinews: muscles; tendons
dread: causing awe or fear
clasp: to hold

When the stars threw down their spears,
  And water'd heaven with their tears,
  Did he smile his work to see?
  Did he who made the Lamb make thee?

Tyger! Tyger! burning bright
  In the forests of the night,
  What immortal hand or eye,
  Dare frame thy fearful symmetry?

A MATTER OF JUSTICE

THE WISDOM OF SOLOMON

retold by Jesse Lyman Hurlbut

A soft answer turns away wrath, but grievous words stir
up anger.

A good name is rather to be chosen than great riches, and
loving favor than silver and gold.

Let another man praise you, and not your own mouth—a
stranger, and not your own lips.

Pride goes before destruction, and a haughty spirit
before a fall.

If your enemy is hungry, give him bread to eat, and if he
is thirsty, give him water to drink, for you will heap coals of
fire upon his head, and the Lord will reward you.

*These sayings come from the book of Proverbs in the Bible, which
records the wisdom of Solomon, a king who reigned in Israel in
the tenth century B.C. Solomon was known far and wide for his
great wisdom. The following story, from the First Book of Kings
in the Bible, tells how Solomon made a wise judgment, though his
reasoning at first might seem surprising.*

Two women came before King Solomon with two little
babies, one dead and the other living. Each claimed the living
child was her own, and said that the dead child belonged to
the other woman. One of the women said, "O my lord, we
two women were sleeping with our children in one bed. And

---

wrath: great anger
grievous: causing pain or grief
haughty: scornfully proud; arrogant

this woman in her sleep lay upon her child, and it died. Then she placed her dead child beside me while I was asleep, and took my child. In the morning I saw that it was not my child, but she says it is mine, and the living child is hers. Now, O king, command this woman to give me my own child."

Then the other woman said, "That is not true. The dead baby is her own, and the living one is mine, which she is trying to take from me."

The young king listened to both women. Then he said, "Bring me a sword."

They brought a sword, and Solomon said, "Take this sword, and cut the living child in two, and give half to one, and half to the other."

Then one woman cried out, and said, "O my lord, do not kill my child! Let the other woman have it, but let the child live!"

But the other woman said, "Let it be neither mine nor yours, but divide it between us."

Then Solomon said, "Give the living child to the woman who would not have it slain, for she is its mother."

And all the people wondered at the wisdom of one so young, and they saw that God had given him understanding.

---

slain: killed

A Just Judge
by Leo Tolstoy

An Algerian king named Bauakas wanted to find out whether or not it was true, as he had been told, that in one of his cities there lived a just judge who could instantly discern the truth and from whom no rogue was ever able to conceal himself. Bauakas exchanged clothes with a merchant and went on horseback to the city where the judge lived.

At the entrance to the city a beggar approached the king and begged alms of him. Bauakas gave him money and was about to continue on his way, but the beggar clung to his clothing.

"What do you wish?" asked the king. "Haven't I given you money?"

"You gave me alms," said the beggar; "now grant me one favor. Let me ride with you as far as the city square; otherwise the horses and camels may trample me."

Bauakas set the beggar behind him on the horse and took him as far as the city square. There he halted his horse, but the beggar refused to dismount.

"We have arrived at the square; why don't you get off?" asked Bauakas.

"Why should I?" the beggar replied. "This horse belongs to me. If you are unwilling to return it, we shall have to go to court."

discern: to recognize or detect; to use intelligence to see or know something
rogue: a rascal; a dishonest person
alms: charity; money or goods given to the poor
dismount: to climb off of

Hearing their quarrel, people gathered around them shouting, "Go to the judge! He will decide between you!"

Bauakas and the beggar went to the judge. There were others in court, and the judge called upon each one in turn. Before he came to Bauakas and the beggar, he heard a scholar and a peasant. They had come to court over a woman: the peasant said she was his wife, and the scholar said she was his. The judge heard them both, remained silent for a moment, and then said, "Leave the woman here with me, and come back tomorrow."

When they had gone, a butcher and an oil merchant came before the judge. The butcher was covered with blood and the oil merchant with oil. In his hand the butcher held some money, and the oil merchant held onto the butcher's hand.

"I was buying oil from this man," the butcher said, "and when I took out my purse to pay him, he seized me by the hand and tried to take all my money away from me. That is why we have come to you—I holding onto my purse, and he holding onto my hand. But the money is mine, and he is a thief."

Then the oil merchant spoke. "That is not true," he said. "The butcher came to me to buy oil, and after I had poured him a full jug, he asked me to change a gold piece for him. When I took out my money and placed it upon a bench, he seized it and tried to run off. I caught him by the hand, as you see, and brought him here to you."

The judge remained silent for a moment, then said, "Leave the money here with me, and come back tomorrow."

scholar: a learned person devoted to study
peasant: a farmer or someone who works on the land

When his turn came, Bauakas told what had happened. The judge listened to him and then asked the beggar to speak.

"All that he said is untrue," said the beggar. "He was sitting on the ground, and as I rode through the city, he asked me to let him ride with me. I set him behind me on my horse and took him where he wanted to go. But when we got there, he refused to get off and said that the horse was his, which is not true."

The judge thought for a moment, then said, "Leave the horse here with me, and come back tomorrow."

The following day many people gathered in court to hear the judge's decisions.

First came the scholar and the peasant.

"Take your wife," the judge said to the scholar, "and the peasant shall be given fifty strokes of the lash."

The scholar took his wife, and the peasant was punished.

Then the judge called the butcher.

"The money is yours," he said to him. And pointing to the oil merchant he said, "Give him fifty strokes of the lash."

He next called Bauakas and the beggar.

"Would you be able to recognize your horse among twenty others?" he asked Bauakas.

"I would," he replied.

"And you?" he asked the beggar.

"I would," said the beggar.

"Come with me," the judge said to Bauakas.

They went to the stable. Bauakas instantly pointed out his horse among the twenty others. Then the judge called the beggar to the stable and told him to point out the horse. The beggar recognized the horse and pointed to it. The judge then returned to his seat.

"Take the horse; it is yours," he said to Bauakas. "Give the beggar fifty strokes of the lash."

When the judge left the court and went home, Bauakas followed him.

"What do you want?" asked the judge. "Are you not satisfied with my decision?"

"I am satisfied," said Bauakas. "But I should like to learn how you knew that the woman was the wife of the scholar, that the money belonged to the butcher, and that the horse was mine and not the beggar's."

"This is how I knew about the woman: in the morning I sent for her and said: 'Please fill my inkwell.' She took the inkwell, washed it quickly and deftly, and filled it with ink; therefore it was work she was accustomed to. If she had been the wife of the peasant, she would not have known how to do it. This showed me that the scholar was telling the truth.

"And this is how I knew about the money: I put it into a cup full of water, and in the morning I looked to see if any oil had risen to the surface. If the money had belonged to the oil merchant it would have been soiled by his oily hands. There was no oil on the water; therefore the butcher was telling the truth.

"It was more difficult to find out about the horse. The beggar recognized it among twenty others, even as you did. However, I did not take you both to the stable to see which of you knew the horse, but to see which of you the horse knew. When you approached it, it turned its head and stretched its neck toward you; but when the beggar touched it, it laid back its ears and lifted one hoof. Therefore I knew that you were the horse's real master."

---

deftly: with skill and ease

Then Bauakas said to the judge, "I am not a merchant, but King Bauakas. I came here in order to see if what is said of you is true. I see now that you are a wise judge. Ask whatever you wish of me, and you shall have it as a reward."

"I need no reward," replied the judge. "I am content that my king has praised me."

OOKA AND THE HONEST THIEF

a Japanese folktale as told by I. G. Edmonds

One day, Yahichi, owner of a rice store, came to Ooka's court, complaining that each night some of his rice disappeared.

"It is such a small amount that I hesitate to trouble your Honorable Honor," Yahichi said, touching the ground with his head to show proper respect for the great magistrate. "But I am reminded of the story of the mountain that was reduced to a plain because a single grain was stolen from it each day for centuries."

Ooka nodded gravely. "It is just as dishonest to steal one grain of rice as it is to steal a large sack," he remarked. "Did you take proper steps to guard your property?"

"Yes, my lord. I stationed a guard with the rice each night, but still it disappears. I cannot understand it," the rice merchant said, pulling his white beard nervously.

"What about your guard. Can he be trusted?" Ooka asked.

"Absolutely, Lord Ooka," Yahichi said. "The guard is Chogoro. He has served my family for seventy-five years."

"Yes, I know Chogoro," Ooka said. "He is a most conscientious man. He could not be the thief. But it is possible that he falls asleep at his post. After all, he is eighty years old."

"A man can be just as alert at eighty as at twenty," Yahichi replied quickly. "I am eighty-one myself, and I have never been so alert. Besides, I stood guard myself with Chogoro these last two nights. The rice vanished just the same."

---

magistrate: a judge
conscientious: careful to act morally and do what is right

"In that case I will watch with you tonight," Ooka said. "I should like to see this for myself."

As he had promised, Ooka made his way that evening to Yahichi's rice store. He was sure that both Yahichi and Chogoro had fallen asleep and had allowed the thief to enter each time the rice had been stolen, and it was not long before his suspicions were proved correct. Within an hour, both men were sleeping soundly. Ooka smiled. He was certain that when the men awoke neither would admit he had slept at all.

A little past midnight, Ooka heard a slight sound outside the building. He sprang to his feet and peered cautiously out the window. To his astonishment, Ooka found himself staring straight into the face of a man standing in the shadows just outside the building. The judge recognized him as Gonta, a laborer who had been out of work for some time. The man was rooted to the spot by fear.

Ooka hesitated to arrest him. After all, he had not entered the rice store. Ooka would have no proof that he had come to steal. He could simply say that he had lost his way in the dark.

Though Ooka had recognized the thief, Gonta had not recognized the judge, for the darkness inside the building hid his face.

Ooka decided the best thing to do would be to pretend that he, too, was a thief. In this way he might trap Gonta into completing his crime. Speaking in a harsh tone to disguise his voice, he said, "You have obviously come here to steal rice just as I have."

Gonta was relieved to find himself face to face with another thief instead of a guard.

"As a favor from one thief to another," Ooka continued, "I will pass the rice out to you, so that you will not need to risk coming in yourself."

Gonta thanked him profusely for his courtesy, and Ooka picked up a large sack of rice and handed it out to him.

"This is too much," Gonta protested. "I want only a few handfuls."

Ooka was amazed. "But if you are going to steal, you may as well take a large amount. After all, if Ooka catches you, you will be punished as much for stealing a single grain as you would for a whole sack."

"That would be dishonest!" Gonta replied indignantly. "I take just enough to feed my family for a single day, for each day I hope I will find work and not have to steal anymore. If I do find work, I intend to return all I have taken."

Then he took out the amount of rice he needed for his family's daily meal and handed the sack back to the astonished judge. Thanking Ooka once more for his courtesy, Gonta turned and disappeared into the darkness. Ooka did not try to stop him.

When the shopkeeper and his guard awoke, Ooka told them what had happened.

"But why did you let the thief go?" Yahichi asked indignantly.

"Gonta is certainly a thief," Ooka replied. "But I am convinced he is an honest one, for he refused to steal more than he needed."

"But, Lord Ooka, how can a man be a thief and honest at the same time?"

---

indignantly: with anger in response to something seen as unjust or mean
courtesy: consideration; politeness

"I would never have believed it possible, but it is so," Ooka said. "It is the duty of a judge to punish wickedness and reward virtue. In this case, we find both qualities in the same man, so obviously it would be unfair to treat him as any ordinary thief."

"But, Lord Ooka—"

"I have made my decision. Tomorrow I will see that work is found for Gonta which is sufficient to feed his family and still leave enough to allow him to pay back the rice he stole. We will see if he keeps his promise. If he returns here and replaces the extra amount each night, it will prove my belief that he is an honest thief."

The plan was carried out according to Ooka's wishes. Gonta was given a job, without knowing that Ooka was responsible. And, as the judge suspected, every night Gonta took the rice left over from his day's earnings and left it in the rice shop.

Ooka put all kinds of obstacles in his way to make it difficult for him to enter the shop, but this did not prevent Gonta from returning each night, although he became more and more afraid of being caught.

Yahichi admitted that the thief had been punished enough for his crime and told Ooka he did not wish to press charges. The great judge smiled and wrote out a small scroll which he ordered Yahichi to leave for Gonta to see when he came to pay for the last portion of rice.

When the honest thief slipped fearfully into the rice shop for the last time, he was shocked to find the scroll on which

---

virtue: goodness
obstacles: barriers; things that get in the way

was written in Ooka's own handwriting, and bearing Ooka's signature, the following message:

> *You owe an extra ten percent for interest. Honesty is the best policy.*

The Convict and the Bishop

from Les Misérables *by Victor Hugo*

Born in France in 1802, Victor Hugo is one of the towering figures of French literature.

His father was a general in the French army. Hugo began to devote himself to literary work when he was nineteen. He wrote several volumes of poems and stories, as well as a number of dramas, which created great excitement among the political parties of France.

In 1837 he was made an officer of the Legion of Honor and held a number of important positions during the next fourteen years. Because of his strong opposition to Emperor Napoleon III, Hugo was banished from France. During his exile he wrote a number of books, among them Les Misérables, *one of the greatest novels ever published. In 1870, after the downfall of Napoleon III, Hugo returned to Paris, where he met with the love and admiration of his countrymen.*

Les Misérables *is a long novel that powerfully depicts human suffering in order to awaken readers to social injustice. The main character of the book is a French peasant, Jean Valjean. After the death of his parents, he goes to live with his widowed sister and helps her support her seven little children. During the severe winter of 1795, he is unable to find work. To save the family from starving, he steals a loaf of bread, but he is caught and sentenced to five years of hard labor. When he repeatedly attempts to escape, his imprisonment is extended by fourteen years.*

In the following selection from the opening of the novel, we meet Jean Valjean when he has finally been released, a man bitter, hardened, and hopeless.

---

banished: sent away permanently; exiled
depicts: portrays; shows

I

An hour before sunset one day in October 1815, a man traveling afoot entered the little town of D—. The few persons who at this time were at their windows or their doors regarded this traveler with a sort of distrust. It would have been hard to find a passer-by more wretched in appearance. He was a man of middle height, stout and hardy. A slouched leather cap half hid his face, bronzed by the sun and wind and dripping with sweat. His shaggy breast was seen through the coarse yellow shirt fastened at the neck by a small silver anchor. He wore a blue cravat twisted like a rope, coarse blue trousers worn and shabby, and an old, ragged, gray blouse patched on one side with a piece of green cloth sewed with twine. Upon his back was a well-filled knapsack. In his hand he carried an enormous knotted stick. His stockingless feet were in hobnailed shoes. His beard was long.

This man must have walked all day, for he appeared very weary. Some women at the lower part of the town had seen him stop under the trees and drink at the fountain at the end of the promenade. He must have been very thirsty, for some children who followed him saw him stop not two hundred steps farther on and drink again at the fountain in the marketplace.

When he reached the mayor's office he went in, and a quarter of an hour afterward he came out. The traveler turned his steps toward the best inn, and went at once into the kitchen, which opened on the street. All the ranges were

---

wretched: poor or miserable
slouched: drooping; hanging down
bronzed: made a yellowish-brown color
cravat: a scarf worn around the neck
promenade: a public path for walking

smoking, and a great fire was burning briskly in the chimney place. The host, who was at the same time head cook, was going from the fireplace to the saucepan, very busy with an excellent dinner for some wagoners who were laughing and talking noisily in the next room. A fat marmot, flanked by white partridges and a goose, was turning on a long spit before the fire; upon the ranges two large carps and a trout were cooking.

The host, hearing the door open and a newcomer enter, said without raising his eyes from the ranges, "What will monsieur have?"

"Something to eat and lodging."

"Nothing more easy," said the host; but on turning his head and taking a look at the traveler, he added, "for pay."

"I have money."

"Then," said the host, "I am at your service."

The man put his wallet back into his pocket, took off his knapsack, and put it down by the door. Holding his stick in his hand, he sat down on a low stool by the fire. However, as the host passed backward and forward he kept a careful eye on the traveler.

"Is dinner almost ready?" asked the man.

"Directly," answered the host.

While the newcomer was warming himself with his back turned, the innkeeper took a pencil from his pocket, and then tore off the corner of an old paper. On the margin he wrote a line or two, folded it, and handed the scrap of paper to a servant. The innkeeper then whispered a word to the boy who ran off in the direction of the mayor's office.

marmot: a groundhog (woodchuck)
monsieur: in French, a respectful form of address for a man,
    meaning "Mister"

The traveler saw nothing of this. He asked a second time, "Is dinner ready?"

"Yes, in a few moments," said the host.

The boy came back with the paper. The host unfolded it hurriedly. He seemed to read with attention, then throwing his head on one side thought for a moment. Then he took a step toward the traveler, who seemed drowned in troubled thought.

"Monsieur," said he, "I cannot receive you."

The traveler half rose from his seat and said, "Why? Are you afraid I shall not pay you, or do you want me to pay in advance? I have money, I tell you."

"It is not that."

"What, then?"

"You have money—"

"Yes," said the man.

"And I," said the host—"I have no room."

"Well, put me in the stable," quietly replied the man.

"I cannot."

"Why not?"

"Because the horses take all the room."

"Well," responded the man, "a corner in the garret—a bed of straw. We will see about that after dinner."

"I cannot give you any dinner."

At this the traveler got up and said, "But I am dying with hunger! I have walked since sunrise; I have traveled twelve leagues. I will pay, and I want something to eat."

"I have nothing," said the host.

The man burst into a laugh and, turning toward the fireplace and the ranges, cried, "Nothing! And all that?"

garret: an attic

leagues: units once used to measure distance (one league = about three miles)

"All that is taken."

"By whom?"

"By those persons, the wagoners."

"How many are there of them?"

"Twelve."

"There is enough there for twenty."

"They have paid for it all in advance."

The man sat down again and said, without raising his voice, "I am at an inn. I am hungry, and I shall stay."

The host bent down to his ear and said in a voice that made him tremble, "Go away!"

At these words the traveler, who was bent over, poking some embers in the fire with his iron-shod stick, turned suddenly around, and as he opened his mouth to reply, the host, looking steadily at him, added in the same low tone, "Stop! No more of that! Shall I tell you your name? Your name is Jean Valjean. Now shall I tell you who you are? When I saw you enter, I suspected something. I sent to the mayor's office, and here is the reply. Can you read?"

So saying, he held toward him the open paper that had just come from the mayor. The man cast a look upon it. The innkeeper, after a short silence, said, "It is my custom to be polite to all. Go!"

The man bowed his head, picked up his knapsack, and went out. He walked at random, slinking near the houses like a sad and humiliated man. He did not once turn around. If he had, he would have seen the innkeeper standing in his doorway, with all his guests and the passers-by gathered about him, speaking excitedly and pointing him out. From the looks of fear and distrust, he would have guessed that before long his arrival would be the talk of the whole town.

random: without a pattern

He saw nothing of all this. People with trouble do not look behind.

He walked along in this way for some time, forgetting fatigue. Suddenly he felt a pang of hunger. Night was at hand, and he looked around to see if he could find a lodging. Just then a light shone at the end of the street. He saw a pine branch hanging by an iron bracket outlined against the twilight sky. He went toward it. The light came from a tavern.

The traveler stopped a moment and looked through the little window into the low hall of the tavern, lighted by a small lamp upon a table, and by a great fire in the chimney place. Some men were drinking, and the host was warming himself. An iron pot hung over the fire, seething in the blaze.

Two doors led into this tavern, one from the street, the other from a small court full of rubbish. The traveler did not dare to enter by the street door; he slipped into the court, stopped again, then timidly raised the latch and pushed open the door.

"Who is it?" asked the host.

"One who wants supper and a bed."

"All right; here you can sup and sleep."

He went in. All the men who were drinking turned toward him. They examined him for some time as he was taking off his knapsack. The lamp shone on one side of his face and the firelight on the other.

The host said to him, "There is the fire; the supper is cooking in the pot. Come and warm yourself, comrade."

---

fatigue: great tiredness; exhaustion
tavern: a place for eating and drinking, often an inn
seething: an old-fashioned word for "boiling"

He seated himself near the fireplace, and stretched his feet
out toward the fire, half dead with fatigue. An inviting odor
came from the pot. All that could be seen of his face under
his slouched cap showed comfort.

However, one of the men at the table was a fisherman
who had put up his horse at the stable of the inn before

coming to the tavern. He had been one of the throng about the innkeeper's doorway half an hour before. He beckoned to the tavern-keeper to come to him. They exchanged a few words in a low voice.

The tavern-keeper then returned to the fire, and laying his hand roughly on the traveler's shoulder said harshly, "You are going to clear out from here."

The stranger turned around and said mildly, "Ah! Do you know?"

"Yes."

"They sent me away from the other inn."

"And we turn you out of this one."

"Where would you have me go?"

"Somewhere else."

The man took up his stick and knapsack and went off. He passed the prison. An iron chain hung from the door, attached to a bell. He rang and the grating opened.

"Monsieur Turnkey," said he, taking off his cap respectfully, "will you open and let me stay here tonight?"

A voice answered, "A prison is not a tavern. Get yourself arrested, and we will open."

The grating closed. The traveler turned into a small street where there were many gardens. In one of them he saw a pretty little one-story house with a light in the window. He looked in as he had done at the tavern. It was a large whitewashed room, with a bed draped in calico, a cradle in the corner, and some wooden chairs. A double-barreled gun hung against the wall. A table was set in the center of the room. A brass lamp lighted the coarse white tablecloth. A tin mug full of wine shone like silver, and the brown soup dish

_____

throng: a crowd
calico: a printed cotton fabric

was smoking. At this table sat a man about forty years old, with a joyous, open countenance; he was bouncing a little child upon his knee. Near him a young woman was nursing another child. The father was laughing, the child was laughing, and the mother was smiling.

The traveler thought that in this happy home he might perhaps find a little pity. He rapped faintly on the window. No one heard him. He rapped a second time. He heard the woman say, "Husband, I think I hear some one rap."

"No," replied the husband.

He rapped a third time. The husband got up, took the lamp, and opened the door. He was a tall man, half peasant, half mechanic. He wore a large leather apron. His shirt, wide and open, showed his bull-like white throat.

"Monsieur," said the traveler, "I beg your pardon. For pay can you give me a plate of soup and a corner of the shed in your garden to sleep in? Tell me—can you, for pay?"

"Who are you?" demanded the master of the house.

The man replied, "I have come from Puy-Moisson. I have walked all day. I have come twelve leagues. Can you, if I pay?"

"I wouldn't refuse to lodge any proper person who would pay," said the peasant, "but why do you not go to the inn?"

"There is no room."

"Bah! That is not possible. It is neither a fair day nor a market day. Have you been there?"

"Yes."

"Well?"

The traveler replied hesitatingly, "I don't know. He didn't take me."

"Have you been to the tavern?"

The stranger stammered, "They didn't take me either."

---

countenance: the expression on one's face

The peasant's face showed distrust. He looked the newcomer over from head to foot, and suddenly exclaimed, with a sort of shudder, "Are you the man?"

He looked again at the stranger, stepped back, put the lamp on the table and took down his gun. His wife, on hearing the words, "Are you the man?" started up, and clasping her two children took refuge behind her husband.

After examining the stranger for a moment as one would a viper, the peasant advanced to the door and said, "Get out!"

"For pity's sake, a glass of water," said the man.

"A gunshot," said the peasant, and then he closed the door violently.

Night came on apace. The cold Alpine winds were blowing. By the light of the waning day the stranger perceived in one of the gardens that fronted the street a kind of hut made of turf. He boldly cleared a wooden fence, and found himself in the garden. He neared the hut. Its door was a narrow, low entrance. It resembled the shanties that road laborers put up. These huts are not usually occupied at night. He got down and crawled into the hut. It was warm there, and he found a good bed of straw. He rested a moment upon this bed, motionless from fatigue; then, as his knapsack on his back troubled him and it would make a good pillow, he began to unbuckle the straps. Just then he heard a ferocious growling, and looking up saw the head of an enormous bulldog at the opening of the hut. It was a dog kennel! Seizing his stick, he made a shield of his knapsack, and got out of the kennel as best he could, but not without enlarging the rents in his already

---

viper: a poisonous snake
apace: quickly
rents: tears or rips

tattered garments. Wary of the dog, he made his way out of the garden backward.

When he had climbed over the fence, he again found himself alone in the street, without shelter, driven even from the straw bed of that wretched dog kennel. He threw himself rather than seated himself on a stone, and exclaimed, "I am not even a dog!"

Then he arose and began to tramp again, taking his way out of town, hoping to find some tree or haystack beneath which to shelter himself. He walked on for some time, his head bowed down. When he thought he was far away from all human habitation, he raised his eyes and looked about him inquiringly.

He was in a field; before him was a low hillock covered with stubble, which after harvest looks like a shaved head. There was nothing in the field nor upon the hill but one ugly tree, a few steps from him. It was so desolate that after a moment he turned back hastily to the road. He retraced his steps to town. The gates were closed. He passed through a breach in the old walls. It was about eight o'clock in the evening. As he did not know the streets he walked at random. When he came to Cathedral Square he shook his fist at the church. At the corner of this square stood a printing office. Exhausted with fatigue, and hoping for nothing better, he lay down on a stone bench in front of this printing office.

Just then an old woman came out of the church. She saw the man lying there in the dark, and said, "What are you doing there, my friend?"

---

garments: clothing
wary: cautious; alert for danger
habitation: where something or someone lives
desolate: deserted and empty
breach: a space or opening

He replied harshly and with anger in his tone, "You see, my good woman, I am going to sleep."

"Upon the bench?" she asked.

"For nineteen years I have had a wooden mattress," said the man. "Tonight I have a stone one."

"You have been a soldier?"

"Yes, my good woman, a soldier."

"Why don't you go to the inn?"

"Because I have no money."

"Alas!" said she. "I have only four sous in my purse."

"Give them, then."

The man took the four sous, and she continued, "You cannot find lodging for so little in an inn, but have you tried? You cannot pass the night so. You must be cold and hungry. They should give you lodging for charity."

"I have knocked at every door."

"Well, what then?"

"Everybody has driven me away."

The good woman touched the man's arm and pointed out to him, on the other side of the square, a little low house beside the bishop's palace.

"You have knocked at every door?" she asked.

"Yes."

"Have you knocked at that one there?"

"No."

"Knock there."

---

bishop: a high official in the church

II

That evening after his walk in the town, the bishop remained quite late in his room. At eight o'clock he was still at work writing, when Madame Magloire came in as usual to take the silverware from the cupboard near the bed. A moment after, the bishop, knowing that the table was laid and that his sister was perhaps waiting, closed his book and went into the dining room.

Just as the bishop entered, Madame Magloire was talking of fastening the front door. It seemed that while she was out getting things for supper, she had heard the news that a suspicious-looking vagabond was lurking somewhere in town, and that every one ought to be careful to shut, bolt, and bar his house properly and to secure his doors thoroughly.

The bishop, having come from a cold room, seated himself before the fire and began to warm himself. He had not heard a word of what Madame Magloire spoke, and so she repeated it.

Then, turning his chair half round and raising to the old servant his good-humored face, he said, "Well, well! What is the matter? Are we in any great danger?"

Then the servant began her story again. "There is a barefooted gypsy man, a sort of dangerous beggar, in town, with a knapsack and a rope and a terrible looking face."

"Indeed!" said the bishop.

"Yes, monseigneur, it is true. Something will happen tonight in the town. Everybody says so. If monseigneur will permit me, I will go and tell the locksmith to come and put the old bolts in the door again."

At this moment there was a violent knock on the door.

"Come in!" said the bishop.

---

vagabond: hobo; homeless wanderer
monseigneur: a French title of respect for a priest

The door opened. A man entered. It was the traveler. He had his knapsack on his back and his stick in his hand. There was a fierce look in his eyes. Leaning with both hands on his club he said in a loud voice, without waiting for the bishop to speak, "See here! My name is Jean Valjean. I was a convict. I have been nineteen years in the galleys. Four days ago I was set free and set out for Pontarlier. For four days I have walked from Toulon. When I reached this place this evening I went to an inn, and they sent me away on account of my yellow passport, which I had to show at the mayor's office. I went to another inn; they said 'Get out!' I went to the prison, and the turnkey would not let me in. I crept into a dog kennel; the dog bit me and drove me away. I went into the fields to sleep beneath the stars. There were no stars, so I came back to town to get shelter in some doorway. In the square I lay down upon a stone. A good woman showed me your house and said, 'Knock there.' I have knocked. What is this place? Are you an inn? I have money. I am very tired and I am so hungry. Can I stay?"

"Madame Magloire," said the bishop, "put on another plate."

The man took three steps and came near the lamp that stood on the table. "Stop!" he exclaimed, as if he had not been understood. "Not that. Did you understand me? I am just out of prison." He drew from his pocket a large sheet of yellow paper, which he unfolded: "There is my passport—yellow, as you see. That is enough to have me kicked out wherever I go. See, here is what they have put in: 'Jean Valjean has been in prison nineteen years. This man is

---

galleys: For a while, in some French seaports, prisoners were housed in old ships called "galleys," after the ships (galleys) that, in earlier times, had been moved mostly by slaves at the oars.

very dangerous.' There you have it! Everybody has thrust me out; will you receive me? Can you give me something to eat, and a place to sleep?"

"Madame Magloire," said the bishop, "put some sheets on the bed in the alcove."

The bishop turned to the man. "Monsieur," he said, "sit down and warm yourself. We are going to have supper presently, and your bed will be made ready while you eat."

At last the man quite understood. His face filled with wonder. He began to stutter like a madman. "True? You will keep me? You won't drive me away? Oh, the fine woman that sent me here! I have money and I will pay well. I beg your pardon; what is your name? You are an innkeeper, aren't you?"

"I am a priest who lives here," said the bishop.

"A priest!" said the man. "Oh, you are the *curé* of this big church. Then you do not ask any money?"

"No," said the bishop; "keep your money."

Madame Magloire brought in a plate and set it on the table. The bishop said to her, "Put this plate as near the fire as you can." Then, turning toward his guest, he added, "The night wind is raw in the Alps; you must be cold, monsieur."

Every time he said this word "monsieur," with his gentle and hospitable voice, the man's face lighted up.

"The lamp," said the bishop, "gives a very poor light."

Madame Magloire understood him, and, going to the bishop's bedchamber, took from the mantel the two silver candlesticks, lighted the candles, and placed them on the table.

---

alcove: a small section of a room set off from the main room
curé: a pastor or clergyman in charge
hospitable: welcoming and friendly
mantel: a shelf over a fireplace

"Monsieur Curé," said the man, "you are good; you do not despise me; you take me into your house; you light your candles for me, and I haven't hid from you where I came from and how miserable I am."

The bishop touched his hand gently and said, "You need not tell me who you are. You are suffering; you are hungry and thirsty; be welcome and do not thank me. Do not tell me that I take you into my house. This is the house of no man except him who needs an asylum. I tell you, who are a traveler, that you are more at home here than I. Whatever is here is yours. What need have I to know your name? Besides, before you told me I knew it."

The man opened his eyes in astonishment and exclaimed, "Really? You knew my name?"

"Yes," answered the bishop; "your name is 'My Brother.'"

"Stop! Stop!" exclaimed the man. "I was famished when I came in, but you are so kind that now I do not know what I am. That is all gone."

The bishop looked at him again and said, "You have seen much suffering?"

"Oh, the ball and chain, the plank to sleep on, the heat, the cold, the lash! The dogs —the dogs are happier!"

"Yes," said the bishop. "You have left a place of suffering. But listen: If you are leaving that sorrowful place with hate and anger against men, you are worthy of compassion; if you leave it with good will, gentleness, and peace, you are better than any of us."

In the meantime, Madame Magloire had served supper. She had without asking added to the usual meal of the bishop a bottle of fine old wine.

---

asylum: a place that takes care of people in need

The bishop's countenance lighted up with pleasure. "To supper!" he said briskly, as was his habit when he had a guest. He seated the man at his right. The bishop's sister, perfectly quiet and natural, took her place at his left. The bishop asked the blessing, and then served the soup himself, according to his usual custom. The man fell to eating greedily.

Suddenly the bishop said, "It seems to me something is lacking on the table."

The fact was that Madame Magloire had set out only the three plates that were necessary. But it was the custom of the house, when the bishop had any one to supper, to set all six of the silver plates on the table—an innocent display.

Madame Magloire understood the remark. Without a word she went out, and a moment afterwards the three plates for which the bishop had asked were shining on the cloth.

The man paid no attention to any one. He ate with the voracity of a starving man. After supper, however, he said, "Monsieur Curé, all this is too good for me, but I must say that the wagoners who wouldn't have me eat with them live better than you."

The bishop replied, "They are more fatigued than I am."

"No," responded the man, "they have more money. You are poor, I can see. Perhaps you are not a curé even. Ah, if God is just, you well deserve to be a curé."

"God is more than just," said the bishop. A moment after, he added, "Monsieur Jean Valjean, you are going to Pontarlier, you say?"

"A compulsory journey. I must be on the road tomorrow morning by daybreak. It is a hard journey. If the nights are cold, the days are warm."

---

voracity: the state of being extremely hungry
compulsory: required or forced

"You are going," said the bishop, "to a fine country. During the Revolution, when my family was ruined, I supported myself there for some time by the labor of my hands. There I found plenty of work, and had only to make my choice. They have in the region where you are going a business which is quite charming. It is dairying. Their dairies are of two kinds: the great barns, belonging to the rich, where there are forty or fifty cows, which produce from seven to eight thousand cheeses during the summer; and the associated dairies, which belong to the poor peasants inhabiting the mountains, who put their cows into a common herd and divide the proceeds. They have a cheese-maker who receives the milk three times a day and notes the quantities."

The traveler became animated while the bishop was describing the good condition of a cheese-maker, as if he wished that this man should understand that one of these dairies would be a good refuge for him.

When the dessert was finished and the bishop had said grace, he turned toward the man and said, "You must be in great need of sleep." Then, after having said good night to his sister, the bishop took one of the silver candlesticks from the table, handed the other to his guest, and said to him, "Monsieur, I will show you to your room." The man followed him.

The house was so arranged that one could reach the alcove only by passing through the bishop's sleeping chamber. Just as they were passing through this room, Madame Magloire was putting up the silver in the cupboard at the head of the bed. It was the last thing she did every night before going to bed.

The bishop left his guest in the alcove before a clean
white bed. The man set the candlestick upon a small table.
"A good night's rest to you," said the bishop. "Tomorrow
morning before you go you shall have a cup of warm milk
from our cows."

"Thank you, monsieur," said the man. Scarcely had he pronounced the words of peace, when suddenly he made a startling motion that would have chilled the two good women of the house if they had seen it. He turned abruptly toward the old man, crossed his arms, and casting a wild look upon his host, exclaimed in a harsh voice, "Ah, now, indeed! You lodge me in your house, as near you as that?" He checked himself, and added with a laugh in which there was something horrible, "Have you reflected upon it? Who tells you that I am not a murderer?"

The bishop responded, "God will take care of that." Then moving his lips like one praying, he raised his right hand and blessed the man, and without looking behind him went to his chamber.

As to the man, he was so completely exhausted that he did not even avail himself of the clean white sheets. He blew out the candle with his nostril, after the manner of convicts, and, dressed as he was, threw himself upon the bed and slept soundly.

Midnight struck, and shortly afterward all in the house slept.

III

As the cathedral clock struck two Jean Valjean awoke. What awakened him was too good a bed. He opened his eyes and looked into the obscurity about him. Many thoughts came to him, but there was one that drove away all others. He had noticed the six silver plates and the large ladle that Madame

---

abruptly: quickly and suddenly
avail himself of: make use of; take the benefit of
obscurity: darkness; shadowy dimness
ladle: a long-handled spoon used for dipping out liquids such as soup

Magloire had put on the table. Those six silver plates took possession of him. There they were, within a few steps. They were solid, and old silver. With the big ladle, they would bring at least two hundred francs—double what he had received after nineteen years of labor.

For a whole hour he struggled with his desire. The clock struck three. He rose up hastily in bed, reached out his arm, and felt his knapsack in the corner of the alcove. Then he thrust out his legs and placed his feet on the floor. Seated on his bed he remained for some time lost in thought. All at once he stooped down, took off his shoes, and put them softly upon the mat in front of the bed. Then he sat still again, and would, perhaps, have remained there until day-break if the clock had not struck the half hour. The clock seemed to say to him, "Come along!" He rose to his feet, hesitated for a moment longer, and listened. All was still in the house. He walked cautiously straight toward the window. The night was not dark. There was a full moon, the glimmer of which was enough to enable him to find his way. On reaching the window he examined it. It had no bars and was fastened with a little wedge only. It overlooked the garden. He opened it, but as the cold keen air rushed into the room, he closed it again immediately.

He looked into the garden with an absorbed look that studies rather than sees. The garden was enclosed by a white wall, quite low and easily scaled. When he had taken this observation, he turned like a man whose mind is made up, went to his alcove, took his knapsack, opened it, fumbled in it, took out something he laid upon the bed, put his shoes into one of his pockets, tied up his bundle, swung it upon his shoulders, and put on his cap. Then he felt for his stick and

---

scaled: climbed

went and put it in the corner of the window. Then he returned to the bed and took up what he had laid on it—a short iron bar pointed at one end like a spear. It was nothing but a miner's drill. He took the drill in his right hand and, holding his breath, moved with stealthy steps toward the door of the bishop's room.

On reaching the door he found it unlatched; the bishop had not closed it. Jean Valjean listened—not a sound. He pushed the door lightly, with the timorous carefulness of a cat. The door yielded to the pressure with a silent movement. He waited a moment, and then pushed the door again more boldly. It yielded gradually and silently. The opening was now wide enough for him to pass through. But there was a small table near the door that blocked the entrance. Jean Valjean saw the obstacle. At all hazards the opening must be made still wider. He pushed the door a third time, harder than before. This time a rusty hinge suddenly sent out into the darkness a harsh and prolonged creak. Jean Valjean shivered. The noise of this hinge sounded in his ears as clear and terrible as the trumpet of the judgment day. For a moment he thought he was lost. He stood still, petrified like the pillar of salt, not daring to stir. He listened. The noise had wakened nobody. This first danger was over, but still he felt within himself a frightful tumult. Nevertheless he did not flinch. His only thought was to make an end of it quickly. He took one step and was in the room.

A deep calm filled the chamber. Jean Valjean advanced, carefully avoiding the furniture. At the farther end of the

---

timorous: shy or fearful

petrified: like the pillar of salt: refers to Bible story of Lot's wife who was turned into a pillar of salt for her disobedience

tumult: confusion; agitation

room he could hear the quiet breathing of the sleeping bishop. Suddenly he stopped. He was near the bed. He had reached it sooner than he thought.

For nearly a half hour a great cloud had darkened the sky. At the moment when Jean Valjean paused before the bed, the cloud broke, as if purposely, and a ray of moonlight crossing the high window suddenly lighted the bishop's pale face. The sleeping bishop appeared as if in a halo. The silence added something strangely solemn to the repose of this venerable man.

Jean Valjean was in the shadow with the iron drill in his hand, erect, motionless, terrified at this radiant figure. He appeared ready either to cleave the bishop's skull or to kiss his hand. In a few moments he raised his left hand slowly to his forehead and took off his cap. The bishop still slept in profoundest peace.

Suddenly Jean Valjean put on his cap, then passed quickly along the bed straight to the cupboard near its head. He raised the drill to force the lock. The key was in it. He opened the cupboard. The first thing he saw was the basket of silver. He took it, crossed the room with hasty stride, careless of noise, reached the door, entered the alcove, took his stick, stepped out, put the silver in his knapsack, threw away the basket, ran across the garden, leaped over the wall like a tiger, and fled.

repose: rest
venerable: highly worthy of respect or reverence
radiant: shining from the reflection of light
cleave: split or cut
profoundest: deepest

IV

The next day at sunrise, the bishop, Monseigneur Bienvenu, was walking in the garden. Madame Magloire ran toward him quite beside herself. "Monseigneur! Monseigneur!" cried she. "Does your honor know where the silver basket is?"

"Yes," said the bishop.

"God be praised!" said she. "I did not know what had become of it."

The bishop had just found the basket on a flowerbed. He gave it to Madame Magloire and said, "There it is."

"Yes," said she, "but there is nothing in it. The silver?"

"Ah!" said the bishop. "It is the silver, then, that troubles you? I do not know where that is."

"Good heavens! It is stolen. That man who came here last night stole it." In the twinkling of an eye Madame Magloire ran inside, went to the alcove, and came back to the bishop, who was bending with some sadness over a flower that the basket had broken in falling.

He looked up at Madame Magloire's cry, "Monseigneur, the man has gone! The silver is stolen!"

The bishop was silent for a moment. Then he said mildly, "Now, first, did the silver belong to us?"

Madame Magloire did not answer. After a moment the bishop continued, "I have for a long time wrongfully withheld this silver. It belonged to the poor. Who was this man? A poor man, evidently."

"Alas! Alas!" returned Madame Magloire. "What is monseigneur going to eat from now?"

"Have we no tin plates?"

"Tin smells."

"Well, then, iron plates."

"Iron tastes."

"Well, then, wooden plates."

In a few minutes the bishop was breakfasting at the same table at which Jean Valjean had sat the night before. He pleasantly remarked to his sister, who said nothing, and to Madame Magloire, who was grumbling to herself, that there was really no need even of a wooden spoon or fork to dip a piece of bread into a cup of milk.

"Was there ever such an idea?" said Madame Magloire to herself as she went backward and forward. "To take in a man like that, and to give him a bed beside him! And yet what a blessing it was that he did nothing but steal! Oh, my stars! It makes the chills run over me when I think of it!"

Just as the brother and sister were rising from the table there was a knock at the door. "Come in," said the bishop.

The door opened. A strange, fierce group appeared on the threshold. Three men were holding a fourth by the collar. The three men were officers; the fourth, Jean Valjean. A brigadier, who appeared to head the group, was near the door. He advanced toward the bishop, giving a military salute. "Monseigneur," said he.

At this word, Jean Valjean, who was sullen and seemed entirely cast down, raised his head with a stupefied air. "Monseigneur!" he murmured. "Then it is not the curé."

"Silence!" exclaimed the brigadier. "It is monseigneur, the bishop."

In the meantime, Monseigneur Bienvenu had approached as quickly as his great age permitted. "Ah! There you are!" said he, looking toward Jean Valjean. "I am glad to see you.

threshold: the doorway; entrance
stupefied: shocked; amazed
brigadier: a military officer

But I gave you the candlesticks also, which are silver like the rest, and would bring two hundred francs. Why did you not take them along with your plates?"

Jean Valjean looked at the bishop with an expression that no human tongue could describe.

"Monseigneur," said the brigadier, "then what this man said was true? We met him. He was going like a man running away, and we arrested him in order to see. He had this silver."

"And he told you," interrupted the bishop with a smile, "that it had been given him by a good old priest with whom he had passed the night. I see it all. And you brought him back here? It is all a mistake."

"If that is so," said the brigadier, "we can let him go,"

"Certainly," replied the bishop.

The officers released Jean Valjean, who shrank back, saying in a voice almost as if he were speaking in his sleep, "Is it true that they let me go?"

"Yes. You may go. Do you not understand?" said the brigadier.

"My friend," said the bishop, "before you go away, here are your candlesticks; take them." He went to the mantelpiece, took the two candlesticks, and brought them to Jean Valjean. The two women beheld the action without a word or gesture or look that might disturb the bishop.

Jean Valjean was trembling in every limb. He took the two candlesticks mechanically, with a wild expression on his face.

"Now," said the bishop, "go in peace. By the way, my friend, when you come again you need not come through the garden. You can always come in and go out by the front door. It is closed only with a latch day and night."

Then, turning to the officers, he said, "Gentlemen, you may retire." The officers withdrew.

Jean Valjean felt like a man about to faint. The bishop approached him and said in a low voice, "Forget not—never forget—that you have promised me to use this silver to become an honest man."

Jean Valjean, who had no recollection of this promise, stood confounded.

The bishop had laid much stress upon these words as he uttered them. He continued solemnly, "Jean Valjean, my brother, you belong no longer to evil, but to good. It is your soul that I am buying for you. I withdraw it from dark thoughts and from the spirit of perdition, and I give it to God."

confounded: very confused; bewildered
perdition: state of being spiritually lost and condemned

MOHANDAS GANDHI: TRUTH IN ACTION
by Vanessa Wright

What is the most powerful force mankind can command? Fire? A great army? Nuclear energy? Mohandas Gandhi answered, "Nonviolence is the greatest force at the disposal of mankind. It is mightier than the mightiest weapon of destruction devised by the ingenuity of man."

But how can the calm voice of nonviolence be heard over the howl of a mob or the whine of bullets? What is the power of truth in an unjust world?

"Thief," thought Mohandas Gandhi. "I am a thief."

Fifteen-year-old Mohandas looked at the gold in his hand. He had stolen it from his brother. It was not his first theft: earlier, he had stolen coins from the family's servants. But now, the gold in his hand burned like a hot coal. He sat down and wrote a letter of confession to his father.

Would his father punish him? Mohandas watched as his father read the note. Tears rolled down his father's cheeks, wetting the paper. But there was no scolding. Silently, his father tore the letter into pieces. Later, Gandhi realized that, in his father's response, he had seen the principle of *Ahimsa*—of nonviolence—in action. He dedicated his life to that principle.

When Gandhi was born in India in 1869, the country was under British rule. As a young man, he sailed to England to

---

at the disposal of: that can be used as one pleases
devised: invented; created; thought up
ingenuity: skill or cleverness in inventing

finish his schooling. In London, he trained to become a lawyer. On his return to India, he struggled to establish his legal career. Since he was meeting with little success in India, he decided to make the long trip to South Africa, where many Indians lived and worked.

He was appalled to find that in some parts of South Africa, Indians were not allowed to vote or to own more than a certain amount of property. They had to be off the streets by 9 p.m., and pay a tax because they were Indian. Once, Gandhi himself purchased a first-class train ticket, only to be told after he had boarded that he had to sit in the third-class compartment reserved for Indians and Africans. When Gandhi refused, he was taken off of the train.

Gandhi knew that such laws were unjust. It was time to tell the truth—and, to take action. So he wrote letters to newspapers, talked with government officials, and held peaceful protests to draw attention to the unjust laws. He also started a group called the Natal Indian Congress, a forum in which Indians in South Africa could discuss the problems facing them and decide how to solve them together.

While he was in South Africa, Gandhi developed the idea of *satyagraha*, a word that means "the pursuit of truth." For Gandhi, satyagraha meant the non-violent struggle against injustice, especially to help those who were poor or suffering due to unjust laws or customs. Gandhi never used violence against his adversaries. Satyagraha meant solving problems peacefully, with respect for all.

---

appalled: horrified; shocked
forum: a place for discussion of ideas
adversaries: enemies

Satyagraha was not an easy path to follow. Once, a mob of white South Africans threw stones and rotten eggs at Gandhi. Officials offered to take the members of the mob to court. But Gandhi refused. "What is the use?" he asked; "I am sure that, when the truth becomes known, they will be sorry for their conduct."

For about twenty years, Gandhi fought for equal rights for Indians in South Africa. During this time, the news spread about his nonviolent struggles, and many people were drawn to the idea of satyagraha.

In 1915, Gandhi returned with his family to India. Little did he know it, but he was about to face one of the greatest challenges of his life.

In his own home country, Gandhi found his people suffering under the rule of the British. The British had been gaining power in India since the mid-1700s, and had officially taken control of India in 1858. Since taking control, Britain had made laws that imposed harsh taxes and stopped Indian trade with other countries. Under these laws, many Indians became poor. The laws were unjust, but with only a few Indians allowed to participate in the government, how could things be changed?

Eventually, many Indians began to demand independence from Britain. But the people were not unified. They spoke different languages, quarreled over religion and social class, and were scattered across the land in cities and tiny villages, long before telephones or the Internet could connect them. The British had a strong government and an army to enforce their laws. To win their independence, the Indians would have to overcome their differences and work together to defeat their common adversary.

It looked as if no one could unite the Indian people. Then one day in January 1915, a large crowd of Indians, rich and poor, from the cities and the villages, and from every social class, gathered around a dock in Bombay. They were there to cheer the man they hoped would lead them to independence as he had led the Indians in South Africa: Mohandas Gandhi.

First, to get reacquainted with his country, Gandhi went around India by train, meeting and talking with the people. He traveled in crowded third-class compartments with hard benches, and sometimes had to sleep standing up. Everywhere he went, he saw poverty and disease.

In 1919, the British passed laws forbidding protest in India. Violence broke out, especially in the city of Amritsar. One British general responded by having his soldiers open fire on a group of men, women, and children in a marketplace. In that terrible incident, 379 people died and more than 1,000 others were injured.

As news of the massacre spread, violence threatened to engulf the entire country. But Gandhi offered another way. He urged Indians to participate in "non cooperation" against the British. Non-cooperation meant that Indians would boycott British goods, take their children out of British schools, and pay not a single rupee of British taxes.

Eventually, faced with the firm and unyielding opposition of hundreds of thousands of Indians, the British began to compromise. Where violence had failed, satyagraha had prevailed. With satyagraha, said Gandhi, "you can bring the world to your feet."

---

reacquainted: introduced to again; familiar with again
massacre: the violent killing of a number of helpless, unresisting people
engulf: to consume or swallow up
boycott: to protest by refusing to buy from or deal with
rupee: an Indian coin
prevailed: triumphed; won

Still, for Gandhi, it was not enough to bring down British rule. He also wanted to build up India from within. So he reached out to the outcasts of Indian society, the poorest of the poor, called the Untouchables.

At that time, most of India's people lived under the caste system. Each person was born into a certain class, or caste, and had to follow its rules. But Untouchables were considered outside the caste system. Everyone shunned them. Members of other castes feared they would be polluted if even the shadow of an Untouchable touched them. But Gandhi called the Untouchables "Children of God" and declared that he would fast until something was done to make their lives better. Through his efforts, Untouchables were allowed into temples and invited to participate in Indian assemblies. And the British agreed never to make any law that called a person an "untouchable."

Still, it was not enough. Gandhi also wanted Indians to be self-sufficient. He burned piles of British clothing in front of Indians, and encouraged them to spin their own cloth and grow their own food or buy it from each other, instead of from the British. He stopped wearing Western clothes, learned to spin cloth, and wore only a cotton shawl and *dhoti*, a kind of loincloth, which had been spun by Indian hands. He also founded communities where people came together to grow their own food, provide for themselves, and work for the good of all the people in the group.

For more than thirty years, Gandhi led the Indians in a non-violent struggle against the British. And at last, in 1947, the British granted Indians their independence. When

---

fast: to go without eating
self-sufficient: able to provide for oneself instead of relying on others

Hindus and Muslims started fighting in India, Gandhi went on a fast to try to bring them together.

Sadly, less than six months after India became independent, Gandhi was assassinated as he walked to a prayer meeting. Millions of people around the world mourned his passing. All his life, Gandhi worked tirelessly against intolerance, violence, and injustice. He helped bring independence and democracy to India. He stood by his principles of truth and nonviolence to make a more just society for India and a better world for all people. The Indian people called him *Mahatma,* which means "great soul," and *Bapu*—"father."

Gandhi's message lived after him. Around the world, champions of human rights still study his ideas and try to use them to help people in their own countries. In the United States, the Reverend Martin Luther King, Jr., once said that Gandhi's words and actions showed him how to use nonviolence to lead the civil rights movement in the 1960s.

"My life is my message," Gandhi once said. "You must be the change you wish to see in the world."

"EQUAL JUSTICE UNDER LAW": THURGOOD MARSHALL

by Mara Rockliff

At his school in Baltimore, Maryland, in the early 1900s, Thurgood Marshall may have been one of the smartest boys in class, but he was not exactly well behaved. If he wasn't throwing chalk or teasing girls, he was arguing with teachers. So, one day, the principal sent him to the basement with a copy of the United States Constitution and stern orders not to come back up till he had memorized a passage.

"Before I left that school," Marshall said many years later, "I knew the whole thing by heart."

Parts of the Constitution, however, confused the young Marshall. For example, the Fourteenth Amendment clearly stated that all Americans must be treated equally under the law. But growing up in Baltimore in the 1920s, Marshall knew that they were not.

Like other Southern states at that time, Maryland enforced a strict system of segregation. Everywhere, African Americans were kept apart—on buses and trains, in restaurants, hotels, and schools. Anything from a water fountain to a movie theater or public park might have a sign saying "Whites Only."

Even the United States Supreme Court supported these unjust laws. In 1896, in the case of *Plessy v. Ferguson,* the Court had ruled that segregation was allowed under the

---

stern: firm and serious

Constitution: the facilities for black Americans, the Court said, simply had to be as good as those for whites—"separate but equal."

In reality, separate almost never meant equal. For example, while Marshall earned high grades in college, the all-white law school of the University of Maryland refused to admit him. (Maryland had no law school for African Americans.) Determined to become a lawyer anyway, he enrolled instead at Howard University in Washington, D.C., one of the few institutions that welcomed African Americans as students.

Marshall left law school eager to win justice for his people. Back in Baltimore, he became known as "the little man's lawyer," often taking on cases without being paid. Soon, the National Association for the Advancement of Colored People (NAACP) asked him to join their legal team. He took charge, becoming known as "Mr. Civil Rights." He helped organize a boycott of businesses that refused to hire African Americans. He successfully sued local school boards that paid black teachers less than half as much as white teachers. He even won a case against the University of Maryland—and the result of the decision was that the university had to admit its first black law student.

In 1950, a group of African American parents in Clarendon County, South Carolina, asked the NAACP for help. Schools in Clarendon County were separate, and far from equal. White children rode buses to modern brick schools with libraries and playgrounds. Black children

facilities: buildings and resources
boycott: to protest by refusing to buy from or deal with

walked miles past the white schools to cramped, unheated wooden shacks without enough desks and chairs—or even any bathrooms.

The parents took the all-white school board to court, hoping to win a decent education for their children. But Marshall wanted more. He wanted to persuade the court that segregation was itself wrong, that the whole idea of "separate but equal" was fundamentally unjust.

To show that segregation made black children feel inferior, Marshall brought in a respected psychologist named Kenneth Clark. Clark described a simple test he had performed on more than two hundred African American children in segregated schools. He showed each child two white dolls and two brown dolls. Then he asked which dolls they liked best. The children said the white dolls were "nice" and "pretty." The brown dolls, they said, were "ugly" and "dirty." When Clark asked one little girl which doll was most like her, she burst into tears.

Despite Clark's dramatic testimony, and other evidence that Marshall presented, the court ruled that Clarendon County could satisfy the law by spending money to improve black schools. In other words, the court allowed the schools to remain separate, and only required that the county spend more money to make them equal. According to this ruling, segregation was still legal.

Marshall was disappointed, but he was not discouraged. He had a new plan—to take the fight against school segregation to the Supreme Court of the United States.

Marshall and his team of lawyers began gathering cases. One was the Clarendon County case. Others came from

---

fundamentally: in the most centrally important way
inferior: less worthy

Virginia, Kansas, Delaware, and Washington, D.C. The whole group of cases was known by the name of the first scheduled to be heard: *Brown v. Board of Education of Topeka, Kansas.*

Marshall faced opposition even within the African American community. Some said that America was not ready for desegregation. "If you challenge 'separate but equal,'" they said, "we might lose even what we have already gained."

Others supported Marshall. "We want our rights now, not a century hence," they said.

Marshall worked tirelessly on the case, hardly stopping to eat or sleep. Finally, on a cold December morning in 1952, Marshall stood looking up at the Supreme Court building. High above him, giant letters carved into the white marble spelled out "Equal Justice Under Law." On this cold day, he hoped he would help those words become reality.

Hundreds of spectators, black and white, crowded the steps. Inside, hundreds more jammed the halls leading to the packed courtroom.

Marshall's opponent was a well-known lawyer named John W. Davis. Marshall greatly admired Davis. As a law student, he had sometimes skipped class to see Davis argue cases before the Supreme Court. Davis seemed unbeatable.

---

hence: from now; in the future

Marshall repeated the argument he had made in South Carolina. Segregation hurt black children. There was no reason for it, other than to keep one race up and the other down. African Americans were not receiving equal treatment under the law.

Davis argued that since the case of *Plessy v. Ferguson,* the Supreme Court had upheld the idea of "separate but equal." Segregation was a fact of Southern life. Why, asked Davis, would black parents want their children in a school where they would be rejected or hated?

In the South, Marshall responded, he had seen white and black children walking down the road together. "They separate and go to different schools," he said, "and they come out and they play together." In other words, children did not choose segregation. They would learn to accept integrated schools.

Davis remained confident. On his way out of the courtroom, he whispered to a colleague, "I think we've got it won."

An exhausted Marshall thought so too. As always, Davis had argued with great skill and poise. And the law was on his side. Marshall had little hope that the Supreme Court would admit that they had been wrong for so many years.

But six months passed, and no decision came. Instead, the Court asked the lawyers on both sides for more information. What, they asked, was the original intent of the Fourteenth Amendment to the Constitution? That amendment says, "No state shall make or enforce any law which shall abridge the

---

colleague: a co-worker
poise: composure; confidence
intent: aim; purpose; goal
abridge: to take away from; to cut from

privileges or immunities of citizens of the United States; nor shall any state . . . deny to any person . . . the equal protection of the laws." The Supreme Court wanted to know: Does that language allow separation of the races? Does the Court have the power to outlaw school segregation?

It was a second chance. Marshall gathered eighty-five experts—historians, sociologists, educators—to help him prepare his answer. Week after week, they planned, talked, and argued together late into the night.

At last, the day arrived. Marshall was ready. In a voice that boomed off the high ceiling of the crowded room, he made his case. Segregation, he argued, was unconstitutional. What reason could there be for separating the two races, he asked, unless the Court found "that for some reason Negroes are inferior to all other human beings"?

As he spoke, Marshall seemed to embody the very point he was arguing. He was knowledgeable, well-spoken, a brilliant lawyer—and African American. Clearly, race had nothing to do with intelligence.

After this second round of arguments was finished, again the months dragged by with no decision from the Court. Marshall went back on the road for the NAACP, trying to raise money to pay the organization's enormous legal bills.

Then, one night in May, after a fundraiser in Mobile, Alabama, the phone rang. Marshall was scheduled to speak in Los Angeles the next day. "Catch the next flight to Washington, D.C.," the caller said—"the Supreme Court is ready to announce its decision."

---

immunities: protections
sociologists: scholars who study the way people function in society

By early afternoon of the next day, Marshall found himself seated, shifting nervously, in the lawyers' section of the Supreme Court.

Chief Justice Earl Warren began to read the Court's opinion. It was long and detailed. He discussed the history of segregation. He gave the legal background. He talked about the importance of education.

Which way had the Court decided? Marshall couldn't tell. He stared at one of the justices, a Southerner. Marshall was sure he would fight for segregation. The justice stared back.

Finally, Chief Justice Warren got to the heart of the matter. Did sending black children to separate schools, no matter how good those schools might be, deprive them of an equal opportunity for education?

Warren concluded, "We believe that it does." To separate some children from others for no reason but skin color, he went on, could "affect their hearts and minds in a way unlikely ever to be undone."

The decision was unanimous. All nine justices agreed: Separate schools could never be equal. Segregation must go.

Marshall said later, "I was so happy I was numb."

Over the course of his career with the NAACP, Thurgood Marshall argued 32 cases before the Supreme Court. He won all but three. And in 1967, President Lyndon Johnson appointed him to the Supreme Court, where he served for 24 years. But to many, *Brown v. Board of Education* remained his greatest victory.

A fellow Supreme Court justice said of Marshall, "No American did more to lead our country out of the wilderness of segregation."

---

shifting: moving from side to side

STORIES FROM THE BIBLE

THE LONG JOURNEY THROUGH THE WILDERNESS

Long ago, a pharaoh made slaves of all the Israelites who lived in Egypt. After many years, the Lord said to one Israelite named Moses, "I have seen the oppression of my people who are in Egypt. I have heard their cry and I know their sorrows. So I have come down to deliver them out of the hand of the Egyptians and to bring them to a good and large land, flowing with milk and honey. Come now, and I will send you to Pharaoh that you may bring the children of Israel out of Egypt."

And Moses did. He led the Israelites out of Egypt and watched with them as Pharaoh's army, which had pursued them, was swallowed by the waters of the sea. The Israelites danced and sang, thinking that the danger had passed and their troubles were over.

But the journey to their ancestors' home, the Promised Land, had just begun.

First, Moses led them into the wilderness, a desolate land of sand and gravel, trapped between steep cliffs and the restless sea. For three days the Israelites walked under the burning sun. Their lips grew cracked and parched for want of water, for not even a trickle sparkled among the rocks.

After three days, they came upon a pool, but the water was foul and no one could drink it. The Israelites called the

---

oppression: the condition of being ruled unjustly and harshly
desolate: bare; lifeless; deserted

place Marah, which means bitterness, and they complained
to Moses, "What shall we drink?"

So Moses cried out to the Lord, and the Lord showed him
a tree. And when Moses cast it into the pool, the water
became sweet, and the Israelites drank it.

Soon, though, the Israelites had also eaten all the food
they had brought with them out of Egypt, and were hungry.
Those who were not brave began to complain to Moses, "Oh,
we wish we had died by the hand of the Lord in Egypt,
where our pots were full of meat and our stomachs full of
bread! For you have brought us into this wilderness to kill us
all with hunger!"

But the Lord said to Moses, "Behold, I will rain bread
from heaven for you. I have heard the complaints of the
children of Israel. Speak to them, saying, 'At twilight, you
shall eat meat, and in the morning, you shall be filled with
bread. And you shall know that I am the Lord your God.'"

That evening, a flock of quail landed near the camp. There
were so many that they covered the land like a blanket. So
the Israelites went among the birds, and caught and ate their
fill. Then, in the morning, the people woke up and saw small
white patches on the ground that looked like frost.

"What is it?" they wondered aloud. "What is it?"

Moses said, "This is the bread that the Lord has given
you to eat."

The people gathered the flakes from the ground and ate
them. They tasted like bread dusted with honey. But they
had to be picked before the sun rose, for then they melted
and disappeared. The Israelites came to call the flakes *manna*.

behold: to see; to look at

From the place where they were fed with quail and manna, Moses led the Israelites farther along the sea toward the mountains. But again they lacked for water, and the Israelites said, "Give us water, Moses! Or did you bring us out of Egypt to kill us with thirst?"

Moses cried to the Lord, "What shall I do with this people? They are almost ready to stone me!"

The Lord said, "Go on before the people. Take with you some of the elders of Israel, and also bring the staff with which you struck the waters in Egypt. I will stand before you on the rock. You shall strike it and water will flow out, so the people may drink."

This Moses did, and the people had water to drink. But while the Israelites rested there, a fierce tribe called the Amalekites roared out of the desert. Mounted on camels and carrying spears, they attacked the Israelites.

Moses called upon a brave young man named Joshua. "Choose a band of men from among the Israelites and begin the fight," he ordered.

While Joshua gathered a small army and attacked the Amalekites, Moses, together with his brother Aaron and a man named Hur, climbed to the top of a nearby hill. When Moses lifted his staff, the Israelites prevailed. But if he lowered the staff, the Amalekites prevailed.

So Moses held up the staff for as long as he could. When he grew tired, Aaron and Hur brought a stone for him to sit upon, and held up his hands until the sun set, and Joshua at last defeated the Amalekites.

The long, hard journey continued. Moses led the Israelites across miles of bare and broken rock. Mountains towered grimly over them. On and on they walked, until they reached

prevailed: triumphed

the peak of Mount Sinai. There, the Lord called to Moses and said, "Say to the children of Israel: 'You have seen what I did to the Egyptians, and how I bore you on eagles' wings. Now, if you will obey my voice and keep my covenant, you shall be a special treasure to me.'"

Moses told the Israelites what the Lord had said to him. Then lightning flashed and thunder rumbled, a thick cloud gathered around the mountain, and the sound of a trumpet rang out, echoing among the hills. Surrounded by smoke, Mount Sinai quaked from its foot to its crown. Moses climbed the mountain, and the Lord told him to carry these words to the Israelites:

> *I am the Lord thy God, who brought thee out of the land of Egypt, out of the house of bondage. Thou shalt have no other gods before me.*
> *Thou shalt not make unto thee any graven image.*
> *Thou shalt not take the name of the Lord thy God in vain.*
> *Remember the Sabbath day, to keep it holy.*
> *Honor thy father and thy mother.*
> *Thou shalt not kill.*
> *Thou shalt not commit adultery.*
> *Thou shalt not steal.*
> *Thou shalt not bear false witness against thy neighbor.*
> *Thou shalt not covet anything that is thy neighbor's.*

Then God gave Moses two small slabs of stone on which were written these Ten Commandments.

Moses returned to the camp and taught the Israelites the Ten Commandments. Later, he went again to hear the Lord

covenant: a formal agreement

on the mountain, and when he returned, he brought the Israelites many other laws and instructions for living together as a people and a nation. After a time, carrying the Ten Commandments before them, the Israelites continued on their journey to the Promised Land.

But the people were tired and began again to complain. "Who will give us meat to eat?" they cried. "We remember the fish we ate freely in Egypt, the cucumbers, the melons, the leeks, the onions, and the garlic. But now our whole being is dried up—there is nothing but all this manna. It was better for us in Egypt!"

They wept and they grumbled and they complained. But still they walked, and still Moses led them, until at last, after many slow marches, the Israelites drew near the Promised Land.

Moses sent twelve scouts ahead to find out what kind of land it was, and what kind of people lived there. When the men returned, they said, "We went to the land where you sent us. It truly flows with milk and honey—and this is its fruit." They held out a cluster of plump grapes, and an armful of ripe pomegranates and figs.

But most of the scouts were scared. "The people there are stronger than we are," they said. "We saw giants living there. We looked like grasshoppers beside them."

The Israelites turned to Moses and cried, "If only we had died in the land of Egypt! Or if only we had died in this wilderness! Why has the Lord brought us to this land to fall by the sword, that our wives and children should become victims? Would it not be better for us to return to Egypt? Let us select a leader and we will return there."

---

pomegranate: a kind of tart, juicy fruit with many seeds

Then two of the scouts, Joshua, who had led the Israelites against the Amalekites in the desert, and a man named Caleb, spoke. "Nonsense!" they said; "we must go into this land at once. It is a good land, and the Lord will bring us into it and give it to us. Do not fear, for the Lord is with us."

Many of the Israelites were shamed and angered by the words of Joshua and Caleb. They threatened to stone the two brave men. Then the Lord said to Moses, "How long will these people reject me? How long shall I bear with these people who complain against me? Say to them, 'Except for Caleb and Joshua, you shall by no means enter the land which I promised I would make you dwell in. But your little ones, whom you said would be victims, I will bring in, and they shall know the land which you have despised.'"

And the Lord sent the Israelites to wander in the desert for forty years. Of them all, only Moses, Joshua, and Caleb survived, together with those who had been born and grew up in the wilderness. When at last the Lord spoke to him, Moses led the children of Israel back to the land east of the River Jordan, across which lay the Promised Land.

Then the Lord said to Moses, "Climb to the top of the mountain I will show you, and see the land which I have given to the children of Israel. When you have seen it, you also shall be gathered to your people."

So Moses gathered the Israelites and spoke to them. He reminded them of their trials and their triumphs, and their long journey through the desert. He told them to keep well their laws and trust in God. He appointed Joshua as their leader, and then he blessed them and said:

---

despised: looked down on; regarded as worthless

Give ear, O heavens, and I will speak,
And hear, O earth, the words of my mouth.
Let my teaching drop as the rain,
My speech distill as the dew,
As raindrops on the tender herb,
And as showers on the grass.
Israel shall dwell in safety,
The fountain of Jacob alone
In a land of grain and new wine,
His heavens shall also drop dew.
Happy are you, O Israel!

Then Moses walked from the plains to the mountaintop. There, the Lord showed him all the land across the River Jordan as far as the western sea, and said, "This is the Promised Land. Now you have seen it with your own eyes— but you shall not cross over there."

And there on the mountaintop, Moses died. The Lord buried him in a valley in the land of Moab, and no one knows his grave to this day.

---

distill: to let fall in drops or as a mist

The Fiery Furnace

Once there lived a king of Babylon called Nebuchadnezzar. During his reign, he attacked the city of Jerusalem, and brought back with him the handsomest and wisest children of Israel to serve in his palace. The king found three of these young men—whom he called Shadrach, Meshach, and Abednego—to be wiser even than all the wise men of Babylon, and so he gave them great power over the land.

It came to pass that King Nebuchadnezzar made a great image covered in gold. When the image was finished, it stood almost a hundred feet high, so Nebuchadnezzar had it set up on a plain outside the city so it could be seen from far away. Then the king commanded all the satraps and governors and treasurers and judges and magistrates, and all other persons in high places in the kingdom, to come to a great gathering where the image would be dedicated for worship.

The great men of the kingdom came from far and near on the appointed day, and stood around the image. Among them were the three young Israelites: Shadrach, Meshach, and Abednego.

Then the king's herald cried, "To you it is commanded, O peoples, nations, and languages, that when you hear the sound of the horn, flute, harp, lyre, and psaltery, and all kinds of music, you shall fall down and worship the gold

image: a statue, in this case meant to represent a deity
satraps: rulers or governors
magistrates: local officials, like judges, who administer law
lyre: a stringed instrument similar to a harp
psaltery: a stringed instrument of ancient times

image that King Nebuchadnezzar has set up. Whoever does not fall down and worship shall be cast immediately into a fiery furnace."

Then came the sound of the horn, flute, harp, lyre, and psaltery, and all kinds of music, and all the people fell down and worshipped the gold image that King Nebuchadnezzar had set up.

All, that is, except for Shadrach, Meshach, and Abednego. They alone stood among the prostrate throng, for they would worship none but the Lord God.

That very day, those men who were jealous of the power of the three Israelites went to the king and said, "O king, live forever! You commanded that when the music sounded everyone should fall down and worship the golden image, and if any man did not worship, he would be thrown into a furnace of fire. There are some Israelites whom you have made rulers in the land who did not do as you commanded. Their names are Shadrach, Meshach, and Abednego. They do not serve your gods or worship the golden image that you set up."

Nebuchadnzzar was filled with rage and fury upon hearing that any had disobeyed his words. He sent for the three men and said to them, "Is it true that you do not serve my gods or worship the gold image that I set up? Was it by purpose that you did not fall down and worship the image of gold? O Shadrach, Meshach, and Abednego, the music shall sound once more, and if you will fall down and worship the image that I have made, then all will be well. But if you do not worship, you shall be cast immediately into a fiery

prostrate: lying flat on the ground, face downward

furnace! And who is the god that shall deliver you from my hands?"

But the young men were not afraid of the king or the furnace. They said, "O Nebuchadnezzar, there is no need for us to answer you. The God whom we serve can save us from the fiery furnace, and he will deliver us from your hand. But if it is God's will that we should die, know, O king, that we do not serve your gods, nor will we worship the gold image you have set up."

This answer made the king even angrier than before. He said, "Make the fire in the furnace seven times hotter than it has ever been before, and bind these men and throw them into it."

Then the soldiers of the king's army seized them, tied them with ropes, dragged them to the mouth of the furnace, and threw them into the fire. The flames rushed out from the open door with such fury that they burned to death the soldiers who held them. And Shadrach, Meshach, and Abednego fell into the heart of the fiery furnace.

King Nebuchadnezzar watched the men fall into the furnace and disappear among the flames. But a moment later, he cried in astonishment, "Did we not throw three men bound into the fire?"

"True, O king," the nobles replied.

"How is it then that I see four men walking in the midst of the fire?" said Nebuchadnezzar. "And lo, they are not hurt, and the fourth man looks like a son of the gods!"

When the flames died down, the king drew near the mouth of the furnace and called out to the men within, "Shadrach, Meshach, and Abednego, servants of the most high God, come forth and come hither."

---

astonishment: amazement; great surprise

So they came out and stood before the king, and all wondered at these men over whom the fire had no power. Their garments had not been scorched, nor their hair singed, nor was there even the smell of fire upon them.

Said Nebuchadnezzar before all his rulers, "Blessed be the God of these men, who sent his angel and delivered his servants who trusted in him!" Then the king commanded that, on pain of death, no one should speak a word against the God of Shadrach, Meshach, and Abednego.

And the king promoted the three young men to even higher positions in the land of Babylon.

hither: here
singed: burned on the surface

THE PARABLE OF THE GOOD SAMARITAN

Jesus said, "Love thy neighbor as thyself," but once a man asked, "Who is my neighbor?"

Jesus answered, "A certain man was going down the lonely road from Jerusalem to Jericho, and he fell into the hands of robbers who took all that he had and beat him. Then they went away, leaving him half dead.

"It happened that a certain priest was going down that road, and when he saw the man lying there, he crossed to the other side of the road and passed by.

"And a Levite, also, when he came to where the man was lying, crossed to the other side of the road and passed by.

"But a Samaritan, as he was going down the road, came to where the man was, and as soon as he saw him, he felt compassion for him. He came to the man, and bound up his wounds, pouring oil and wine over them. Then he lifted him up, set him on his own donkey, and walked beside him to an inn. There he took care of him all night, and the next morning he took out from his purse two coins, and gave them to the innkeeper and said, 'Take care of him, and if you need to spend more than this, do so, and when I come again I will pay it to you.'

"Which one of these three, do you think, showed himself a neighbor to the man who fell among the robbers?"

The man said, "The one who showed mercy on him."

Then Jesus said, "Go, and do thou likewise."

Samaritan: a native of the region in the ancient Middle East called Samaria

STORIES OF OUR TIME

THANK YOU, M'AM

by Langston Hughes

She was a large woman with a large purse that had everything in it but a hammer and nails. It had a long strap, and she carried it slung across her shoulder. It was about eleven o'clock at night, dark, and she was walking alone, when a boy ran up behind her and tried to snatch her purse. The strap broke with the sudden single tug the boy gave it from behind. But the boy's weight and the weight of the purse combined caused him to lose his balance. Instead of taking off full blast as he had hoped, the boy fell on his back on the sidewalk and his legs flew up. The large woman simply turned around and kicked him right square in his blue-jeaned sitter. Then she reached down, picked the boy up by his shirt front, and shook him until his teeth rattled.

After that the woman said, "Pick up my pocketbook, boy, and give it here."

She still held him tightly. But she bent down enough to permit him to stoop and pick up her purse. Then she said, "Now ain't you ashamed of yourself?"

Firmly gripped by his shirt front, the boy said, "Yes'm."

The woman said, "What did you want to do it for?"

The boy said, "I didn't aim to."

She said, "You a lie!"

By that time two or three people passed, stopped, turned to look, and some stood watching.

"If I turn you loose, will you run?" asked the woman.

"Yes'm," said the boy.

"Then I won't turn you loose," said the woman. She did not release him.

"Lady, I'm sorry," whispered the boy.

"Um-hum! Your face is dirty. I got a great mind to wash your face for you. Ain't you got nobody home to tell you to wash your face?"

"No'm," said the boy.

"Then it will get washed this evening," said the large woman, starting up the street, dragging the frightened boy behind her.

He looked as if he were fourteen or fifteen, frail and willow-wild, in tennis shoes and blue jeans.

The woman said, "You ought to be my son. I would teach you right from wrong. Least I can do right now is to wash your face. Are you hungry?"

"No'm," said the being-dragged boy. "I just want you to turn me loose."

"Was I bothering you when I turned that corner?" asked the woman.

"No'm."

"But you put yourself in contact with me?" said the woman. "If you think that that contact is not going to last awhile, you got another thought coming. When I get through with you, sir, you are going to remember Mrs. Luella Bates Washington Jones."

Sweat popped out on the boy's face and he began to struggle. Mrs. Jones stopped, jerked him around in front of her, put a half nelson about his neck, and continued to drag him up the street. When she got to her door, she dragged the boy inside, down a hall, and into a large kitchenette-furnished room at the rear of the house. She switched on the light and left the door open. The boy could hear other roomers laughing and talking in the large house. Some of their doors were open, too, so he knew he and the woman were not alone. The woman still had him by the neck in the middle of her room.

She said, "What is your name?"

"Roger," answered the boy.

"Then, Roger, you go to that sink and wash your face," said the woman, whereupon she turned him loose—at last. Roger looked at the door—looked at the woman—looked at the door—and went to the sink.

"Let the water run until it gets warm," she said. "Here's a clean towel."

"You gonna take me to jail?" asked the boy, bending over the sink.

"Not with that face, I would not take you nowhere," said the woman. "Here I am trying to get home to cook me a bite to eat, and you snatch my pocketbook! Maybe you ain't been to your supper either, late as it be. Have you?"

"There's nobody home at my house," said the boy.

"Then we'll eat," said the woman. "I believe you're hungry—or been hungry—to try to snatch my pocketbook!"

"I want a pair of blue suede shoes," said the boy.

"Well, you didn't have to snatch my pocketbook to get some suede shoes," said Mrs. Luella Bates Washington Jones. "You could of asked me."

"M'am?"

The water dripping from his face, the boy looked at her. There was a long pause. A very long pause. After he had dried his face and not knowing what else to do, dried it again, the boy turned around, wondering what next. The door was open. He could make a dash for it down the hall. He could run, run, run, *run!*

The woman was sitting on the daybed. After a while she said, "I were young once and I wanted things I could not get."

There was another long pause. The boy's mouth opened. Then he frowned, not knowing he frowned.

The woman said, "Um-hum! You thought I was going to say *but,* didn't you? You thought I was going to say, *but I didn't snatch people's pocketbooks.* Well, I wasn't going to say that." Pause. Silence. "I have done things, too, which I would not tell you, son—neither tell God, if He didn't already know. Everybody's got something in common. So you set down while I fix us something to eat. You might run that comb through your hair so you will look presentable."

In another corner of the room behind a screen was a gas plate and an icebox. Mrs. Jones got up and went behind the screen. The woman did not watch the boy to see if he was going to run now, nor did she watch her purse, which she left behind her on the daybed. But the boy took care to sit on the far side of the room, away from the purse, where he thought she could easily see him out of the corner of her eye if she wanted to. He did not trust the woman not to trust him. And he did not want to be mistrusted now.

"Do you need somebody to go to the store," asked the boy, "maybe to get some milk or something?"

"Don't believe I do," said the woman, "unless you just want sweet milk yourself. I was going to make cocoa out of this canned milk I got here."

"That will be fine," said the boy.

---

presentable: worthy of being seen by others

She heated some lima beans and ham she had in the icebox, made the cocoa, and set the table. The woman did not ask the boy anything about where he lived, or his folks, or anything else that would embarrass him. Instead, as they ate, she told him about her job in a hotel beauty shop that stayed open late, what the work was like, and how all kinds of women came in and out, blondes, redheads, and Spanish. Then she cut him a half of her ten-cent cake.

"Eat some more, son," she said.

When they were finished eating, she got up and said, "Now here, take this ten dollars and buy yourself some blue suede shoes. And next time, do not make the mistake of latching onto my pocketbook nor nobody else's—because shoes got by devilish ways will burn your feet. I got to get my rest now. But from here on in, son, I hope you will behave yourself."

She led him down the hall to the front door and opened it. "Good night! Behave yourself, boy!" she said, looking out into the street as he went down the steps.

The boy wanted to say something other than, "Thank you, m'am," to Mrs. Luella Bates Washington Jones, but although his lips moved, he couldn't even say that as he turned at the foot of the barren stoop and looked up at the large woman in the door. Then she shut the door.

---

barren: bare

THE CIRCUIT
by Francisco Jimenez

It was that time of year again. Ito, the strawberry sharecropper, did not smile. It was natural. The peak of the strawberry season was over and the last few days the workers, most of them braceros, were not picking as many boxes as they had during the months of June and July.

As the last days of August disappeared, so did the number of braceros. Sunday, only one—the best picker— came to work. I liked him. Sometimes we talked during our half-hour lunch break. That is how I found out he was from Jalisco, the same state in Mexico my family was from. That Sunday was the last time I saw him.

When the sun had tired and sunk behind the mountains, Ito signaled us that it was time to go home. "Ya esora," he yelled in his broken Spanish. Those were the words I waited for twelve hours a day, every day, seven days a week, week after week. And the thought of not hearing them again saddened me.

As we drove home Papá did not say a word. With both hands on the wheel, he stared at the dirt road. My older brother, Roberto, was also silent. He leaned his head back and closed his eyes. Once in a while he cleared from his throat the dust that blew in from outside.

Yes, it was that time of year. When I opened the front door to the shack, I stopped. Everything we owned was neatly

sharecropper: a farmer who rents land and uses a share of the crops
   to pay the rent
braceros: Mexican laborers who work seasonally on farms
Ya esora: Spanish for "It's time," or "Time's up."

packed in cardboard boxes. Suddenly I felt even more the weight of hours, days, weeks, and months of work. I sat down on a box. The thought of having to move to Fresno and knowing what was in store for me there brought tears to my eyes.

That night I could not sleep. I lay in bed thinking about how much I hated this move.

A little before five o'clock in the morning, Papá woke everyone up. A few minutes later, the yelling and screaming of my little brothers and sisters, for whom the move was a great adventure, broke the silence of dawn. Shortly, the barking of the dogs accompanied them.

While we packed the breakfast dishes, Papá went outside to start the "Carcanchita." That was the name Papá gave his old '38 black Plymouth. He bought it in a used-car lot in Santa Rosa in the winter of 1949. Papá was very proud of his little jalopy. He had a right to be proud of it. He spent a lot of time looking at other cars before buying this one. When he finally chose the "Carcanchita," he checked it thoroughly before driving it out of the car lot. He examined every inch of the car. He listened to the motor, tilting his head from side to side like a parrot, trying to detect any noises that spelled car trouble. After being satisfied with the looks and sounds of the car, Papá then insisted on knowing who the original owner was. He never did find out from the car salesman, but he bought the car anyway. Papá figured the original owner must have been an important man because behind the rear seat of the car he found a blue necktie.

---

jalopy: an old, run-down car

Papá parked the car out in front and left the motor running. "Listo," he yelled. Without saying a word, Roberto and I began to carry the boxes out to the car. Roberto carried the two big boxes and I carried the two smaller ones. Papá then threw the mattress on top of the car roof and tied it with ropes to the front and rear bumpers.

Everything was packed except Mamá's pot. It was an old large galvanized pot she had picked up at an army surplus store in Santa Maria the year I was born. The pot had many dents and nicks, and the more dents and nicks it acquired the more Mamá liked it. "Mi olla," she used to say proudly.

I held the front door open as Mamá carefully carried out her pot by both handles, making sure not to spill the cooked beans. When she got to the car, Papá reached out to help her with it. Roberto opened the rear car door and Papá gently placed it on the floor behind the front seat. All of us then climbed in. Papá sighed, wiped the sweat off his forehead with his sleeve, and said wearily: "Es todo."

As we drove away, I felt a lump in my throat. I turned around and looked at our little shack for the last time.

At sunset we drove into a labor camp near Fresno. Since Papá did not speak English, Mamá asked the camp foreman if he needed any more workers. "We don't need no more," said the foreman, scratching his head. "Check with Sullivan down the road. Can't miss him. He lives in a big white house with a fence around it."

When we got there, Mamá walked up to the house. She went through a white gate, past a row of rose bushes, up the

---

listo: Spanish for "ready"
galvanized: coated with zinc
Mi olla: Spanish for "My kettle"
Es todo: Spanish for "That's everything."

stairs to the front door. She rang the doorbell. The porch light went on and a tall husky man came out. They exchanged a few words. After the man went in, Mamá clasped her hands and hurried back to the car. "We have work! Mr. Sullivan said we can stay there the whole season," she said, gasping and pointing to an old garage near the stables.

The garage was worn out by the years. It had no windows. The walls, eaten by termites, strained to support the roof full of holes. The dirt floor, populated by earthworms, looked like a gray road map.

That night, by the light of a kerosene lamp, we unpacked and cleaned our new home. Roberto swept away the loose dirt, leaving the hard ground. Papá plugged the holes in the walls with old newspapers and tin can tops. Mamá fed my little brothers and sisters. Papá and Roberto then brought in the mattress and placed it in the far corner of the garage. "Mamá, you and the little ones sleep on the mattress. Robert, Panchito, and I will sleep outside under the trees," Papá said.

Early next morning Mr. Sullivan showed us where his crop was, and after breakfast, Papá, Roberto, and I headed for the vineyard to pick.

Around nine o'clock the temperature had risen to almost one hundred degrees. I was completely soaked in sweat and my mouth felt as if I had been chewing on a handkerchief. I walked over to the end of the row, picked up the jug of water we had brought, and began drinking. "Don't drink too much; you'll get sick," Roberto shouted. No sooner had he said that than I felt sick to my stomach. I dropped to my knees and let the jug roll off my hands. I remained motionless with my eyes glued on the hot sandy ground. All I could hear was the

husky: big and burly

drone of insects. Slowly I began to recover. I poured water over my face and neck and watched the dirty water run down my arms to the ground.

I still felt a little dizzy when we took a break to eat lunch. It was past two o'clock and we sat underneath a large walnut tree that was on the side of the road. While we ate, Papá jotted down the number of boxes we had picked. Roberto drew designs on the ground with a stick. Suddenly I noticed Papá's face turn pale as he looked down the road. "Here comes the school bus," he whispered loudly in alarm. Instinctively, Roberto and I ran and hid in the vineyards. We did not want to get in trouble for not going to school. The neatly dressed boys about my age got off. They carried books under their arms. After they crossed the street, the bus drove away. Roberto and I came out from hiding and joined Papá. "Tienen que tener cuidado," he warned us.

After lunch we went back to work. The sun kept beating down. The buzzing insects, the wet sweat, and the hot dry dust made the afternoon seem to last forever. Finally the mountains around the valley reached out and swallowed the sun. Within an hour it was too dark to continue picking. The vines blanketed the grapes, making it difficult to see the bunches. "Vamonos," said Papá, signaling to us that it was time to quit work. Papá then took out a pencil and began to figure out how much we had earned our first day. He wrote down numbers, crossed some out, wrote down some more. "Quince," he murmured.

---

instinctively: naturally; spontaneously
Tienen que tener cuidado: Spanish for "You have to be careful."
Vamonos: Spanish for "Let's go."
quince: Spanish for "fifteen"

When we arrived home, we took a cold shower underneath a waterhose. We then sat down to eat dinner around some wooden crates that served as a table. Mamá had cooked a special meal for us. We had rice and tortillas with "carne con chile," my favorite dish.

The next morning I could hardly move. My body ached all over. I felt little control over my arms and legs. This feeling went on every morning for days until my muscles finally got used to the work.

It was Monday, the first week of November. The grape season was over and I could now go to school. I woke up early that morning and lay in bed, looking at the stars and savoring the thought of not going to work and of starting sixth grade for the first time that year. Since I could not sleep, I decided to get up and join Papá and Roberto at breakfast. I sat at the table across from Roberto, but I kept my head down. I did not want to look up and face him. I knew he was sad. He was not going to school today. He was not going tomorrow, or next week, or next month. He would not go until the cotton season was over, and that was sometime in February. I rubbed my hands together and watched the dry, acid stained skin fall to the floor in little rolls.

When Papá and Roberto left for work, I felt relief. I walked to the top of a small grade next to the shack and watched the "Carcanchita" disappear in the distance in a cloud of dust.

Two hours later, around eight o'clock, I stood by the side of the road waiting for school bus number twenty. When it arrived I climbed in. Everyone was busy either talking or yelling. I sat in an empty seat in the back.

---

carne con chile: a spicy dish of meat with beans
savoring: deeply enjoying

When the bus stopped in front of the school, I felt very nervous. I looked out the bus window and saw boys and girls carrying books under their arms. I put my hands in my pant pockets and walked to the principal's office. When I entered I heard a woman's voice say: "May I help you?" I was startled. I had not heard English for months. For a few seconds I remained speechless. I looked at the lady who waited for an answer. My first instinct was to answer her in Spanish, but I held back. Finally, after struggling for English words, I managed to tell her that I wanted to enroll in the sixth grade. After answering many questions, I was led to the classroom.

Mr. Lema, the sixth grade teacher, greeted me and assigned me a desk. He then introduced me to the class. I was so nervous and scared at that moment when everyone's eyes were on me that I wished I were with Papá and Roberto picking cotton. After taking roll, Mr. Lema gave the class the assignment for the first hour. "The first thing we have to do this morning is finish reading the story we began yesterday," he said enthusiastically. He walked up to me, handed me an English book, and asked me to read. "We are on page 125," he said politely. When I heard this, I felt my blood rush to my head; I felt dizzy. "Would you like to read?" he asked hesitantly. I opened the book to page 125. My mouth was dry. My eyes began to water. I could not begin. "You can read later," Mr. Lema said understandingly.

For the rest of the reading period I kept getting angrier and angrier with myself. I should have read, I thought to myself.

During recess I went into the restroom and opened my English book to page 125. I began to read in a low voice, pretending I was in class. There were many words I did not know. I closed the book and headed back to the classroom.

Mr. Lema was sitting at his desk correcting papers. When I entered he looked up at me and smiled. I felt better. I walked up to him and asked if he could help me with the new words. "Gladly," he said.

The rest of the month I spent my lunch hours working on English with Mr. Lema, my best friend at school.

One Friday during lunch hour Mr. Lema asked me to take a walk with him to the music room. "Do you like music?" he asked me as we entered the building.

"Yes, I like corridos," I answered. He then picked up a trumpet, blew on it and handed it to me. The sound gave me goose bumps. I knew that sound. I had heard it in many corridos. "How would you like to learn how to play it?" he asked. He must have read my face because before I could answer, he added: "I'll teach you how to play it during our lunch hours."

That day I could hardly wait to get home to tell Papá and Mamá the great news. As I got off the bus, my little brothers and sisters ran up to meet me. They were yelling and screaming. I thought they were happy to see me, but when I opened the door to our shack, I saw that everything we owned was neatly packed in cardboard boxes.

---

corridos: traditional Mexican and Mexican-American songs that tell stories

THE BRACELET

by Yoshiko Uchida

"**M**ama, is it time to go?" I hadn't planned to cry, but the tears came suddenly and I wiped them away with the back of my hand. I didn't want my older sister to see me crying.

"It's almost time, Ruri," my mother said gently. Her face was filled with a kind of sadness I had never seen before.

I looked around at the empty room. The clothes Mama always told me to hang up in the closet, the junk piled on my dresser, the old rag doll I could never bear to part with— they were all gone. There was nothing left in my room, and there was nothing left in the rest of the house. The rugs and furniture were gone, the pictures and drapes were down, and the closets and cupboards were empty. The house was like a gift box after the nice thing inside was gone; just a lot of nothingness.

It was almost time to leave our home, but we weren't moving to a nicer house or to a new town. It was April 21, 1942. The United States and Japan were at war, and every Japanese person on the West Coast was being evacuated by the government to a concentration camp. Mama, my sister Keiko, and I were being sent from our home, and out of Berkeley, and eventually out of California.

The doorbell rang, and I ran to answer it before my sister could. I thought maybe by some miracle a messenger from the government might be standing there, tall and proper and buttoned into a uniform, come to tell us it was all a terrible

---

evacuated: removed; withdrawn

mistake, that we wouldn't have to leave after all. Or maybe the messenger would have a telegram from Papa, who was interned in a prisoner-of-war camp in Montana because he had worked for a Japanese business firm.

The FBI had come to pick up Papa and hundreds of other Japanese community leaders on the very day that Japanese planes had bombed Pearl Harbor. The government thought they were dangerous enemy aliens. If it weren't so sad, it would have been funny. Papa could no more be dangerous than the mayor of our city, and he was every bit as loyal to the United States. He had lived here since 1917.

When I opened the door, it wasn't a messenger from anywhere. It was my best friend, Laurie Madison, from next door. She was holding a package wrapped up like a birthday present, and she wasn't wearing her party dress, and her face drooped like a wilted tulip.

"Hi," she said. "I came to say goodbye."

She thrust the present at me and told me it was something to take to camp. "It's a bracelet," she said before I could open the package. "Put it on so you won't have to pack it." She knew I didn't have one inch of space left in my suitcase. We had been instructed to take only what we could carry into camp, and Mama had told us we could each take only two suitcases.

"Then how are we ever going to pack the dishes and blankets and sheets they've told us to bring with us?" Keiko worried.

"I don't really know," Mama had said, and she simply began packing those big impossible things into an enormous

telegram: a message sent electronically over telegraph wires
interned: confined; held
aliens: people from a foreign country
wilted: drooping from lack of water

duffle bag, along with umbrellas, boots, a kettle, hot plate, and flashlight.

"Who's going to carry that huge sack?" I asked.

But Mama didn't worry about things like that. "Someone will help us," she said. "Don't worry." So I didn't.

Laurie wanted me to open her package and put the bracelet on before she left. It was a thin gold chain with a heart dangling on it. She helped me put it on, and I told her I'd never take it off, ever.

"Well, goodbye then," Laurie said awkwardly. "Come home soon."

"I will," I said, although I didn't know if I would ever get back to Berkeley again.

I watched Laurie go down the block, her long blond pigtails bouncing as she walked. I wondered who'd be sitting in my desk at Lincoln Junior High now that I was gone. Laurie kept turning and waving, even walking backward for a while, until she got to the corner. I didn't want to watch anymore, and I slammed the door shut.

The next time the doorbell rang, it was Mrs. Simpson, our other neighbor. She was going to drive us to the Congregational Church, which was the Civil Control Station where all the Japanese of Berkeley were supposed to report.

It was time to go. "Come on, Ruri. Get your things," my sister called to me.

It was a warm day, but I put on a sweater and my coat so I wouldn't have to carry them and I picked up my two suitcases. Each one had a tag with my name and our family number on it. Every Japanese family had to register and get a number. We were Family Number 13453.

Mama was taking one last look around our house. She was going from room to room, as though she were trying to take a mental picture of the house she had lived in for fifteen years, so she would never forget it.

I saw her take a long last look at the garden that Papa loved. The irises beside the fish pond were just beginning to bloom. If Papa had been home, he would have cut the first iris blossom and brought it inside to Mama. "This one is for you," he would have said. And Mama would have smiled and said, "Thank you, Papa San," and put it in her favorite cut-glass vase.

But the garden looked shabby and forsaken now that Papa was gone and Mama was too busy to take care of it. It looked the way I felt, sort of empty and lonely and abandoned.

When Mrs. Simpson took us to the Civil Control Station, I felt even worse. I was scared, and for a minute I thought I was going to lose my breakfast right in front of everybody. There must have been over a thousand Japanese people gathered at the church. Some were old and some were young. Some were talking and laughing, and some were crying. I guess everybody else was scared too. No one knew exactly what was going to happen to us. We just knew that we were being taken to the Tanforan Racetracks, which the army had turned into a camp for the Japanese. There were fourteen other camps like ours along the West Coast.

What scared me the most were the soldiers standing at the doorway of the church hall. They were carrying guns with mounted bayonets. I wondered if they thought we would try to run away and whether they'd shoot us or come after us with their bayonets if we did.

A long line of buses waited to take us to camp. There were trucks too, for our baggage. And Mama was right; some men

---

forsaken: abandoned
bayonets: blades attached to the ends of rifles

were there to help us load our duffel bag. When it was time to board the buses, I sat with Keiko, and Mama sat behind us. The bus went down Grove Street and passed the small Japanese food store where Mama used to order her bean-curd cakes and pickled radish. The windows were all boarded up, but there was a sign still hanging on the door that read, "We are loyal Americans."

The crazy thing about the whole evacuation was that we were all loyal Americans. Most of us were citizens because we had been born here. But our parents, who had come from Japan, couldn't become citizens because there was a law that prevented any Asian from becoming a citizen. Now everybody with a Japanese face was being shipped off to concentration camps.

"It's stupid," Keiko muttered as we saw the racetrack looming up beside the highway. "If there were any Japanese spies around, they'd have gone back to Japan long ago."

"I'll say," I agreed. My sister was in high school and she ought to know, I thought.

When the bus turned in to Tanforan, there were even more armed guards at the gate, and I saw barbed wire strung around the entire grounds. I felt as though I were going into a prison, but I hadn't done anything wrong.

We streamed off the buses and poured into a huge room, where doctors looked down our throats and peeled back our eyelids to see if we had any diseases. Then we were given our housing assignments. The man in charge gave Mama a slip of paper. We were in Barrack 16, Apartment 40.

"Mama!" I said. "We're going to live in an apartment!" The only apartment I had ever seen was the one my piano

---

evacuation: the removal of a group of people

teacher lived in. It was an enormous building in San Francisco, with an elevator and thick carpeted hallways. I thought how wonderful it would be to have our own elevator. A house was all right, but an apartment seemed elegant and special.

We walked down the racetrack, looking for Barrack 16. Mr. Noma, a friend of Papa's, helped us carry our bags. I was so busy looking around I slipped and almost fell on the muddy track. Army barracks had been built everywhere, all around the racetrack and even in the center oval.

Mr. Noma pointed beyond the track toward the horse stables. "I think your barrack is out there."

He was right. We came to a long stable that had once housed the horses of Tanforan, and we climbed up the wide ramp. Each stall had a number painted on it, and when we got to number 40, Mr. Noma pushed open the door.

"Well, here it is," he said, "Apartment 40." The stall was narrow and empty and dark. There were two small windows on each side of the door. Three folded army cots were on the dust-covered floor, and one light bulb dangled from the ceiling. That was all. This was our apartment, and it still smelled like horses.

Mama looked at my sister and then at me. "It won't be so bad when we fix it up," she began. "I'll ask Mr. Simpson to send me some materials for curtains. I could make some cushions too, and…well…" She stopped. She couldn't think of anything more to say.

Mr. Noma said he'd go get some mattresses for us. "I'd better hurry before they're all gone." He rushed off. I think he wanted to leave so that he wouldn't have to see Mama cry. But he needn't have run off, because Mama didn't cry.

She just went out to borrow a broom and began sweeping out the dust and dirt. "Will you girls set up the cots?" she asked.

It was only after we'd put up the last cot that I noticed my bracelet was gone. "I've lost Laurie's bracelet!" I screamed. "My bracelet's gone!"

We looked all over the stall and even down the ramp. I wanted to run back down to the track and go over every inch of ground we'd walked on, but it was getting dark and Mama wouldn't let me.

I thought of what I'd promised Laurie. I wasn't ever going to take the bracelet off, not even when I went to take a shower. And now I had lost it on my very first day in camp. I wanted to cry.

I kept looking for it all the time we were in Tanforan. I didn't stop looking until the day we were sent to another camp called Topaz, in the middle of a desert in Utah. And then I gave up.

But Mama told me never mind. She said I didn't need a bracelet to remember Laurie, just as I didn't need anything to remember Papa or our home in Berkeley or all the people and things we loved and had left behind.

"Those are things we can carry in our hearts and take with us no matter where we are sent," she said.

And I guess she was right. I've never forgotten Laurie, even now.

THE STRANGERS THAT CAME TO TOWN
by Ambrose Flack

The first of April was dark and stormy. Silver whips of lightning were cracking open low-hanging clouds. My brother Tom and I were recovering from chest colds. Tired of listening to the radio, we turned to the big living-room window of our house on Syringa Street.

"Here they come, Mother," yelled Tom when a truck drove up in the rain and stopped at the empty cottage across the street.

Mother hurried in from the kitchen, and we three looked out. That truck, we knew, contained the Duvitch family and all their earthly possessions.

All afternoon Mother, Tom, and I had been watching for them with mixed emotions. For the Duvitches had just come over from Europe, and they were the first of the nationality to settle in our town.

A stream of children, accompanied by a big brown dog, poured out of the back of the truck and stood in a huddle in the rain. Mr. Duvitch and the biggest boy carefully helped Mrs. Duvitch from the seat and walked her into the house.

"I wonder if Mrs. Duvitch is ill," murmured Mother.

"She must be," said Tom. "I wonder if it would be all right for Andy and me to help them move in their stuff."

Mother shook her head. It was a strict family rule that any illness which kept us out of school also kept us indoors.

Yet the Duvitches got along very well without help from us. Every child pitched in and helped carry all the boxes and bundles into the house. In no time at all, it seemed, the truck was empty, and the Duvitches were settled in their new home.

That was the signal for Mother to step into the kitchen. She returned carrying a basket containing a roast chicken, steaming hot, a loaf of homemade bread, and a pie. These she took to the house across the street and gave to the boy who answered her knock.

The next day when Mother was fixing lunch, we heard a faint tap at the back door. I answered it, and there, holding Mother's basket, stood a pale, dark-eyed boy in a faded shirt and patched overalls.

In the basket were the empty dishes, all of which shone, and a tiny, very shapely, potted rose tree covered with delicate pinktipped buds. It was a beautiful plant—the first of its kind to be seen in our neighborhood.

"I send them a basket of food," Mother said slowly, deeply touched, "and get this queenly gift."

She stopped to visit the Duvitches a week later. But the boy who opened the door said, "Mamma sick. She stay in bed today."

Mrs. Duvitch never came to visit us, so Mother made no further attempts to see the family. But Father disagreed when she said that she thought the Duvitches wanted their Syringa Street neighbors to leave them alone.

Syringa Street seemed to be a friendly street, but from the start the Duvitches were marked people. They were the one poor, struggling family in the midst of a prosperous

marked: set apart; visibly different
prosperous: wealthy

community. It didn't take people long to start talking about how different they were.

At school everyone made fun of the thick black-bread sandwiches the Duvitch boys ate for lunch. And the girls stared and pointed at their boiled-out, ragpickers' clothes, obviously salvaged from the dump on the outskirts of town.

Mr. Duvitch's job in the local meatpacking plant made his walk home an odoriferous one. The Syringa Street youngsters, meeting him on the street, would hold their noses as he walked by.

The Duvitches' dog Kasimar behaved just like the family to which he belonged. He seemed to be afraid of his own shadow, and nobody had ever heard him bark or growl.

But Mother, remembering the potted rose tree, always had a friendly word and a smile for the young Duvitches. And she always managed to find a bone for Kasimar when he scraped up the courage to venture across Syringa Street.

One fine Saturday in July, two years after the Duvitches had moved in, Father took Tom and me on a camping trip to Durston's Pond. The pond was only four miles north of town and was an excellent place for swimming and fishing.

We often had the quiet little pond all to ourselves. But on our arrival that afternoon we found the Duvitches in possession. Mr. Duvitch and the younger boys were casting from shore. The older sons were fishing for bass from a flat-bottomed rowboat.

Tom and I ignored the Duvitch boys. But Father went up to Mr. Duvitch and put out his hand.

---

ragpickers: people who collect and sell rags and other discarded items for a living
salvaged: rescued from wreckage or ruin
odoriferous: bad-smelling
venture: to undertake or proceed in something risky

"Hello, Mr. Duvitch. It's nice to see you and the boys here."

Mr. Duvitch was a lean little man with watery blue eyes and a kicked-about look. Gratitude for being agreeably noticed showed in his face as he shook Father's hand.

"I know the mosquitoes are biting," Father went on pleasantly. "But are the fish?"

Proudly, oh so proudly, Mr. Duvitch exhibited the catch that would probably feed his family for a week. He had a fine catch of bass, perch, and sunfish, all of them alive, swimming around in the oaken washtub into which they'd been dropped.

Father told Mr. Duvitch that we couldn't hope to do as well but we'd try.

We three pitched our tent on a little hill beside the pond and rented a rowboat for the afternoon. Then Father, with a happy sigh, lay down on the blanket for a nap.

Tom and I got into our bathing suits, and for a while we stayed out in the boat, fishing. Feeling hot and sweaty later on, we rowed to shore to fetch towels and soap from the tent so we could wash.

On our way back to the water, we stopped to look at the fish still swimming around in the oaken tub. The Duvitches had moved on and were now fishing in a small arm of the pond just below us. They had their back to us and were almost out of sight.

Tom and I, our glances meeting over the big cake of soap in my hand, were similarly and wickedly tempted. We held a brief, whispered conversation. Then, egged on by Tom and quite willing on my own, I played a shameful trick on the Duvitches. Without considering further, I dropped the cake of soap into the tub of fish.

"Let's go," whispered Tom after we had watched the soap sink.

We raced back to the tent, had some sandwiches, and played ball for a while. Later on, we swam out to the deep water. Tom scrambled up on a floating log and dived off. I tried to climb on, too, but kept tumbling back into the water.

While we were splashing around, the Duvitches returned to the spot on shore where they had left their tub of fish. Soon Tom and I heard their muffled cries of disbelief and dismay.

Then we saw Father get up, walk over to them, and look down at the tub of fish near his feet. In a moment he motioned to Tom and me to come ashore at once.

Looking as guilty as we felt, we swam in and joined the group around the tub. In the midst of our stricken neighbors stood Father, holding the half-melted cake of soap in his palm.

The fish had perished miserably in the soapy water and were unfit to eat. Not only had Tom and I snatched precious food from the Duvitches' mouths, but we had also revealed the scorn we felt for them.

Father's eyes were narrow slits of blue fire in his white face. I had never seen him so angry. One look at Tom and me told him everything.

"You will begin," Father said in a voice I didn't recognize, "by saying you're sorry."

Tom and I stumbled through our apologies, trying to avoid looking at the Duvitches.

"Do you realize," Father went on coldly, "that in certain primitive communities the sort of stunt you've pulled would be punishable by death?"

"Turn over the tub," Father said sharply.

We turned it over. The gray soapy water ran away in bubbly streams, disappearing into the ground. And the poisoned fish lay exposed on the grass—quiet, strangled, open-mouthed.

"Count the fish," Father ordered, his voice like steel.

Tom and I got down on our knees.

"How many are there?" demanded Father.

"Sixty-one," I said.

"How many bass?"

"Twelve."

"Get into the rowboat," Father said in the same steely tones. "You are not to come back until you've caught sixty-one fish to repay Mr. Duvitch. See to it that among them you bring in at least a dozen bass."

Father stepped up to the tent to fetch our shirts and blue jeans. Rolling them into a tight ball, he threw them angrily into the rowboat. He then turned his back on us and stalked away.

Tom and I lost no time in rowing out on the pond. We dropped anchor, threaded our steel rods, and, baiting our hooks, began to fish. I knew that if it took us all summer to catch them, we dared not set foot ashore without sixty-one fish. Almost at once Tom pulled in a good-sized bass, and ten minutes later two yellow perch were added to our string.

The crestfallen Duvitches went home. Father threw himself down on the blanket. That was about four in the afternoon.

Oh, the mosquitoes! They were bad enough while the light held. But as evening came on, millions of them swarmed out of the swampland surrounding the pond.

After an hour of it we wanted to leap overboard. They got in our ears, our noses, even our mouths. Nestling in our hair,

---

crestfallen: very upset; saddened

they bit through to our scalps. Several times we slipped over the side of the boat, ducking under the water to escape the bloodthirsty swarms.

The night dragged on while the whining clouds of mosquitoes grew thicker.

"Andy, what time is it?"

"Ten o'clock, Tom."

"Is that all?" Tom groaned. He pulled in another bass and then killed six or eight mosquitoes with one slap. Two hours passed, and midnight was ghostly on the pond.

The moon sailed high in the purple sky, casting a great white shaft of quivering radiance on the water. But sitting on a hard rowboat seat, aching with tiredness, it all seemed like a nightmare.

"Andy, what time is it?"

"Two o'clock, Tom."

The treetops whispered in the breeze. Owls hooted— mockingly, we thought—and bats circled over our heads. Our only comfort was the campfire Father kept burning near the tent. The bright flame flared like a beacon light in the dark. We went on fishing as our tormentors bit and sang.

Each hour took forever to pass, and I fairly panted for the light of dawn to come.

"Andy—"

"It's four o'clock, Tom, and we've got sixteen fish."

Dawn finally came. But a long stretch on Durston's Pond in the blistering July heat still faced us.

The rising sun cast glistening circles of rose-colored light on the windless surface of the pond. The mosquitoes thinned. The fish continued to bite, but as we fished, the sun mounted steadily. And by eleven o'clock it had become a ball of fire in the cloudless sky. Tom and I began to bake in the heat waves that shimmered over the pond.

"I wish it were night again, Andy," groaned Tom after sweating out an hour of it. "This is worse than the mosquitoes."

I tore a piece of cloth from my shirt and made it into a cap. "Take this, and cover your head, Tom," I said, handing it to him. "We might get sunstrokes and faint."

"I don't care if I do," Tom said feebly. "I'd rather be unconscious."

No breeze stirred. No cloud shadowed the pond. Even the bird life of the swamp, usually bursting with melody, was silent and motionless. Tom was drooping visibly in the glare, and I tried hard not to look at his scorched face.

Between three and four o'clock we dropped lines in a school of yellow perch and pulled up no fewer than twenty. The bass continued to bite in the deep black holes off the swamp, which bristled with tree trunks. Aching, blistered, moving like machines, Tom and I geared ourselves for the home stretch.

When the sun, dropping low, had lost its fury, and the sky began to pale, I pulled up the thirteenth bass. That bass was our sixty-first fish.

Drooping from lack of food and sleep, Tom and I rowed to shore where Father was waiting.

He received us coolly, making no comment on our condition. At once he asked to see the fish, and we held them up by the string.

"Count them," he said.

Obviously we would receive permission to land only when we had produced the required number.

"Sixty-one," said Tom, "including thirteen bass."

"Very good," said Father in businesslike tones. "We will now restore to Mr. Duvitch his rightful property."

I stumbled out of the boat, aching all over. But somehow something inside me was rejoicing. I guess that Father was secretly proud of Tom and me. And I realized, too, that all through the night he had suffered with us.

We drove in silence to the Duvitch cottage. There we found Mr. Duvitch sitting alone on the front porch.

When he saw Tom and me and we silently handed him the strings of fish, he gulped and swallowed hard. Then in a voice raw with emotion he protested that he had not wished us to suffer so.

"Will you shake hands with the boys?" asked Father.

Instead Mr. Duvitch broke down. Tom and I did not know where to look. During those moments we suffered more intensely than we had suffered in the clouds of mosquitoes and under the blazing sun. After our neighbor had composed himself, he seized our hands and bowed his head over them. Tom and I swallowed hard.

Then we went home to Mother, who had heard about our ordeal on the pond from one of the neighbors. When she saw Tom and me she burst into tears. She tried to embrace us, but we drew back painfully. Soon she had us plastered with a thick coating of soothing sunburn cream.

In bed our skin stuck to the sheets and pillowcases, but we slept as if we had been drugged.

We woke up around noon the next day. "It is high time," I heard Father say calmly to Mother, "for this senseless feeling against the Duvitches to stop. And I'm willing to do my part.

---

composed: calmed; settled
ordeal: an extremely difficult or painful experience
plastered: covered heavily and thickly, as if with plaster

"Tonight we're having supper with them. Mr. Duvitch said that since Andy and Tom caught the fish, he'd feel better if we all shared them. After a few hints from me, he invited us over. It may be a trial, but we ought to be able to bear it."

We walked across the street at six o'clock, not knowing what to expect. The Duvitches, dressed in their Sunday best, bright and shining as we had never seen them, received us as if we were royalty. They looked at Tom and me—and then delicately looked away.

I shuddered when I thought of what we would have had to endure had this been any other family.

The young Duvitches, thrilled by their first party and by the family's first acceptance in this country, kept showing their pleasure in wide, delighted smiles. I couldn't believe they were the same, timid, downcast youngsters I had known at school.

We ate fried fish at a long plank table in the back yard. Father kept the conversation going. As he told stories and jokes, we discovered that the Duvitches had a gift for gaiety. And how they loved to laugh.

After supper David played folk songs on his accordion. Mr. Duvitch turned out to be something of a ventriloquist. He made the dog Kasimar talk in Polish and the cat Jan talk in German.

I could tell that the Duvitch family was a great surprise to Father and that he had enjoyed the evening tremendously.

"To think," he murmured as we crossed the street, "that they should turn out to be people of courtesy and accomplishment." Father sighed and shook his head.

---

downcast: sad; low-spirited

ventriloquist: one who speaks without moving his lips and projects his
    voice to make it seem as though it is coming from somewhere else

"They're being looked down on and ignored by their inferiors."

After that evening things began to improve for the Duvitches. Our neighbors looked up to Father and often followed his lead since he was the only college graduate on Syringa Street. They decided that if the Duvitches were good enough for a highly educated man like Father, they were good enough for them. So they started inviting Mr. and Mrs. Duvitch to the community parties.

It wasn't long before the Duvitch boys and girls started making friends in the community. David was invited to play his accordion at a country dance, and he ended up being one of the town's most popular musicians.

The other Duvitch youngsters taught their folk dances to the boys and girls at school. Even Kasimar began to take on the ways of an American dog, daring to bark and growl on occasion.

Syringa Street presently had reason to be grateful to Mrs. Duvitch, who turned out to have a great gift for nursing. In times of severe illness, the doctor invariably suggested that she be sent for. When Mrs. Duvitch slipped into a sickroom, she never failed to bring along an air of peace. After an hour or two, the patient was calmed and the family reassured.

Soon people began to turn to the Duvitches with all kinds of problems. The elder Duvitches, with their Old World wisdom, would sit by the hour and talk gently and convincingly against fear, false pride, disgrace, and grief.

One winter day, Mr. Duvitch gave Father a pair of handsome, fur-lined mittens—just the right size for Father's enormous hands. After our neighbor had left, Father drew on the mittens, which had a slightly ashy odor.

"Probably one of the boys found them in an ash heap at the dump," Father remarked. "But why should I value them any the less? Who would have dreamed that the Duvitches would have so much more to offer us than we have to offer them?"

---

invariably: constantly; regularly without change
Old World: a nickname for Europe (as distinguished from America as the "New World")

POETRY

"TO EVERYTHING THERE IS A SEASON"

WAITING
by Harry Behn

Dreaming of honeycombs to share
With her small cubs, a mother bear
Sleeps in a snug and snowy lair.

Bees in the drowsy, drifted hive
Sip hoarded honey to survive
Until the flowers come alive.

Sleeping beneath the deep snow
Seeds of honeyed flowers know
When it is time to wake and grow.

lair: the home of a wild animal
hoarded: saved up, stored away

SOMETHING TOLD THE WILD GEESE
by Rachel Field

Something told the wild geese
    It was time to go.
Though the fields lay golden
    Something whispered, "Snow."
Leaves were green and stirring,
    Berries, luster-glossed,
But beneath warm feathers
    Something cautioned, "Frost."
All the sagging orchards
    Steamed with amber spice,
But each wild breast stiffened
    At remembered ice.
Something told the wild geese
    It was time to fly—
Summer sun was on their wings,
    Winter in their cry.

---

luster-glossed: shiny with light
amber: a warm yellow-brown color

Six Haiku
translated by Harry Behn

Broken and broken
again on the sea, the moon
so easily mends.

—Chosu

Watching the full moon,
a small hungry boy forgets
to eat his supper.

—Basho

Behind me the moon
brushes a shadow of pines
lightly on the floor.

—Kikaku

Out of the sky, geese
come honking in the spring's cold
early-morning light.

—Soin

O foolish ducklings,
you know my old green pond is
watched by a weasel!

—Buson

A spark in the sun,
this tiny flower has roots
deep in the cool earth

—written by Harry Behn

CHECK

by James Stephens

The Night was creeping on the ground!
She crept and did not make a sound,

Until she reached the tree: And then
She covered it, and stole again

Along the grass beside the wall!
—I heard the rustling of her shawl

As she threw blackness everywhere
Along the sky, the ground, the air,

And in the room where I was hid!
But, no matter what she did

To everything that was without,
She could not put my candle out!

So I stared at the Night! And she
Stared back solemnly at me!

---

solemnly: seriously and sternly

THE PASTURE
by Robert Frost

I'm going out to clean the pasture spring;
I'll only stop to rake the leaves away
(And wait to watch the clear water, I may):
I shan't be gone long.—You come too.

I'm going out to fetch the little calf
That's standing by the mother. It's so young
It totters when she licks it with her tongue.
I shan't be gone long.—You come too.

---

shan't: contraction for "shall not"
totters: stands unsteadily; wobbles

A WINTRY SONNET

by Christina Rossetti

A Robin said: The Spring will never come,
    And I shall never care to build again.
A Rosebush said: These frosts are wearisome,
    My sap will never stir for sun or rain.
The half Moon said: These nights are fogged and slow,
    I neither care to wax nor care to wane.
The Ocean said: I thirst from long ago,
    Because earth's rivers cannot fill the main.—
When Springtime came, red Robin built a nest,
    And trilled a lover's song in sheer delight.
Grey hoarfrost vanished, and the Rose with might
    Clothed her in leaves and buds of crimson core.
The dim Moon brightened. Ocean sunned his crest,
    Dimpled his blue,—yet thirsted evermore.

---

wearisome: tiring
trilled: sang
hoarfrost: frost
crimson: dark red

THE MORNS ARE MEEKER THAN THEY WERE

by Emily Dickinson

The morns are meeker than they were—
The nuts are getting brown—
The berry's cheek is plumper—
The Rose is out of town.

The Maple wears a gayer scarf—
The field a scarlet gown—
Lest I should be old fashioned
I'll put a trinket on.

---

meeker: milder; gentler
gayer: brighter; more cheerful
scarlet: bright red
lest: for fear that
trinket: a small ornament, such as piece of jewelry

THE STORM
by Walter de la Mare

First there were two of us, then there were three of us,
Then there was one bird more,
Four of us—wild white sea-birds,
Treading the ocean floor;
And the wind rose, and the sea rose,
To the angry billows' roar—
With one of us—two of us—three of us—four of us
Sea-birds on the shore.

Soon there were five of us, soon there were nine of us,
And lo! in a trice sixteen!
And the yeasty surf curdled over the sands,
The gaunt gray rocks between;
And the tempest raved, and the lightning's fire
Struck blue on the spindrift hoar—
And on four of us—ay, and on four times four of us
Sea-birds on the shore.

---

billows: large waves
in a trice: an expression meaning "in an instant"
yeasty: bubbly like yeast
gaunt: barren
tempest: a wild storm
spindrift: sea spray
hoar: from *hoary* = gray or white

And our sixteen waxed to thirty-two,
And they to past three score—
A wild, white welter of winnowing wings,
And ever more and more;
And the winds lulled, and the seas went down,
And the sun streamed out on high,
Gilding the pools and the spume and the spars
'Neath the vast blue deeps of the sky;

And the isles and the bright green headlands shone,
As they'd never shone before,
Mountains and valleys of silver cloud,
Wherein to swing, sweep, soar—
A host of screeching, scolding, scrabbling
Sea-birds on the shore—
A snowy, silent, sun-washed drift
Of sea birds on the shore.

---

waxed: increased
score: twenty
welter: state of confusion; chaos
winnowing: blowing; fanning
lulled: calmed down
gilding: turning a golden color
spume: foam
spars: poles that support the rigging (ropes) of a sailing ship
isles: islands

SWIFT THINGS ARE BEAUTIFUL
by Elizabeth Coatsworth

Swift things are beautiful:
Swallows and deer,
And lightning that falls
Bright-veined and clear,
Rivers and meteors,
Wind in the wheat,
The strong-withered horse,
The runner's sure feet.

And slow things are beautiful:
The closing of day,
The pause of the wave
That curves downward to spray,
The ember that crumbles,
The opening flower,
And the ox that moves on
In the quiet of power.

---

strong-withered: strong backed (*withers* are the highest part of
   a horse's back)
ember: a glowing coal

I Wandered Lonely as a Cloud

by William Wordsworth

I wandered lonely as a cloud
    That floats on high o'er vales and hills,
When all at once I saw a crowd,—
    A host of golden daffodils
Beside the lake, beneath the trees,
Fluttering and dancing in the breeze.

Continuous as the stars that shine
    And twinkle on the Milky Way,
They stretched in never-ending line
    Along the margin of a bay:
Ten thousand saw I, at a glance,
Tossing their heads in sprightly dance.

The waves beside them danced, but they
    Outdid the sparkling waves in glee;
A poet could not but be gay
    In such a jocund company;
I gazed—and gazed—but little thought
What wealth the show to me had brought.

vales: valleys
host: a great many
margin: edge
sprightly: spirited; lively
glee: joy; delight
jocund: merry; happy

For oft, when on my couch I lie,
　　In vacant or in pensive mood,
They flash upon that inward eye
　　Which is the bliss of solitude;
And then my heart with pleasure fills,
And dances with the daffodils.

---

oft: often
vacant: without activity
pensive: thoughtful
bliss: joy; great happiness
solitude: the state of being alone

Until I Saw the Sea

by Lilian Moore

Until I saw the sea
I did not know
that wind
could wrinkle water so.

I never knew
that sun
could splinter a whole sea of blue.

Nor
did I know before
a sea breathes in and out
upon a shore.

splinter: to split into thin pieces

"To everything there is a season"
(Ecclesiastes 3:1-8; King James version)

To everything there is a season, and a time for every
    purpose under heaven:
A time to be born, and a time to die; a time to plant,
    and a time to pluck up what is planted.
A time to kill, and a time to heal; a time to break down,
    and a time to build up;
A time to weep, and a time to laugh; a time to mourn,
    and a time to dance;
A time to cast away stones, and a time to gather stones together;
    a time to embrace, and a time to refrain from embracing;
A time to get, and a time to lose; a time to keep,
    and a time to cast away;
A time to rend, and a time to sew; a time to keep silence,
    and a time to speak;
A time to love, and a time to hate; a time of war,
    and a time of peace.

---

refrain: to keep from doing; to hold back
rend: to rip apart

STUFF AND NONSENSE

LEWIS CARROLL:
THE MATHEMATICIAN WHO IMAGINED ALICE

Charles Lutwidge Dodgson, better known by his pen name, Lewis Carroll, was born January 27, 1832. The son of a clergyman, Charles grew up in the countryside of England, some distance from the little village of Daresbury. The neighborhood was so secluded that even the passing of a cart was an interesting event. It is likely, however, that the home was not a quiet one, since it housed eleven boys and girls.

Charles, the oldest son, was a bright and clever boy who invented games for the entertainment of his brothers and sisters, and delighted them with magic tricks and puppet shows. When Charles was eleven years old the family moved to Yorkshire, and a year later he was sent from home to school. His schoolmaster found him a "gentle, intelligent, well-conducted boy." On his fourteenth birthday, Charles entered Rugby, the most famous of the English preparatory schools. He excelled in his work, especially in mathematics. But as a shy, studious boy who often stammered, he was sometimes bullied by the older boys, so his years here were not happy.

From Rugby Charles Dodgson went to Christ Church College at Oxford University. At Christ Church, as student, tutor, and lecturer, he spent the remainder of his life. The

---

clergyman: a minister
secluded: isolated, apart from others
well-conducted: well-behaved
preparatory schools: schools that prepare students for academic study at
    a university

routine of his days was very simple and regular. He spent the mornings in his lecture room, the afternoons in the country or on the river, and the evenings with his books, either reading or preparing for the next day's work.

He was a great favorite with children, inventing puzzles, games, and stories for their amusement, just as he had for his brothers and sisters many years ago. One July afternoon in 1862, Dodgson and a friend went for a boating trip and picnic with three of the children of the dean of Christ Church College. Along the way, Dodgson entertained the girls—Ina, Edith, and Alice—with a wonderful story about the adventures of a little girl named Alice. At the request of his young friends, Dodgson afterwards wrote out this story, and called it *Alice's Adventures Underground.* In 1865, it was published with the title *Alice's Adventures in Wonderland,* under the pen name of Lewis Carroll. (Dodgson made up his pen name by turning his first two names, Charles Lutwidge, into Latin—"Carolus Lodovicus"—from which he got "Lewis Carroll.")

Alice's Adventures in Wonderland became at once a classic, widely read in England and America, and translated into French, German, Italian, and other languages.

Dodgson wrote several other popular books for children, the best known of which is *Through the Looking-Glass,* a continuation of Alice's adventures. Besides these stories for children, he wrote several scholarly works on mathematics, with titles such as *A Syllabus of Plane Algebraic Geometry.* It was hard for people to realize that Charles Dodgson, the mathematician, and Lewis Carroll, the author of the charming tales for children, were one and the same person.

Selections from

ALICE'S ADVENTURES IN WONDERLAND

by Lewis Carroll

DOWN THE RABBIT-HOLE

Alice was beginning to get very tired of sitting by her sister on the bank, and of having nothing to do: once or twice she had peeped into the book her sister was reading, but it had no pictures or conversations in it, "And what is the use of a book," thought Alice, "without pictures or conversations?"

So she was considering, in her own mind (as well as she could, for the hot day made her feel very sleepy and stupid), whether the pleasure of making a daisy-chain would be worth the trouble of getting up and picking the daisies, when suddenly a White Rabbit with pink eyes ran close by her.

There was nothing so *very* remarkable in that; nor did Alice think it so very much out of the way to hear the Rabbit say to itself, "Oh dear! Oh dear! I shall be too late!" (when she thought it over afterward, it occurred to her that she ought to have wondered at this, but at the time it all seemed quite natural); but, when the Rabbit *actually took a watch out of its waistcoat-pocket,* and looked at it, and then hurried on, Alice started to her feet, for it flashed across her mind that she had never before seen a rabbit with either a waistcoat-pocket, or a watch to take out of it, and, burning with curiosity, she ran

waistcoat: a vest
started: moved suddenly; jumped
marmalade: fruit preserve; jam

across the field after it, and was just in time to see it pop down a large rabbit-hole under the hedge.

In another moment down went Alice after it, never once considering how in the world she was to get out again.

The rabbit-hole went straight on like a tunnel for some way, and then dipped suddenly down, so suddenly that Alice had not a moment to think about stopping herself before she found herself falling down what seemed to be a very deep well.

Either the well was very deep, or she fell very slowly, for she had plenty of time as she went down to look about her, and to wonder what was going to happen next. First, she tried to look down and make out what she was coming to, but it was too dark to see anything: then she looked at the sides of the well, and noticed that they were filled with cupboards and bookshelves: here and there she saw maps and pictures hung upon pegs. She took down a jar from one of the shelves as she passed: it was labeled "ORANGE MARMALADE," but to her great disappointment it was empty: she did not like to drop the jar, for fear of killing somebody underneath, so managed to put it into one of the cupboards as she fell past it.

---

marmalade: fruit preserve; jam

"Well!" thought Alice to herself. "After such a fall as this, I shall think nothing of tumbling down stairs! How brave they'll all think me at home! Why, I wouldn't say anything about it, even if I fell off the top of the house!" (Which was very likely true.)

Down, down, down. Would the fall *never* come to an end? "I wonder how many miles I've fallen by this time?" she said aloud. "I must be getting somewhere near the center of the earth. Let me see: that would be four thousand miles down, I think—" (for, you see, Alice had learned several things of this sort in her lessons in the school-room, and though this was not a very good opportunity for showing off her knowledge, as there was no one to listen to her, still it was good practice to say it over) "—yes, that's about the right distance—but then I wonder what Latitude or Longitude I've got to?" (Alice had not the slightest idea what Latitude was, or Longitude either, but she thought they were nice grand words to say).

Presently she began again. "I wonder if I shall fall right *through* the earth! How funny it'll seem to come out among the people that walk with their heads downward! The antipathies, I think—" (she was rather glad there was no one listening, this time, as it didn't sound at all the right word) "—but I shall have to ask them what the name of the country is, you know. Please, Ma'am, is this New Zealand? Or Australia?" (and she tried to curtsey as she spoke—fancy, *curtseying* as you're falling through the air! Do you think you could manage it?) "And what an ignorant little girl she'll think me for asking! No, it'll never do to ask: perhaps I shall see it written up somewhere."

---

antipathies: Alice has confused *antipathies* (strong dislikes) for *antipodes* (any two opposite points on the earth, such as the North and South Poles).

Down, down, down. There was nothing else to do, so Alice soon began talking again. "Dinah'll miss me very much tonight, I should think!" (Dinah was the cat.) "I hope they'll remember her saucer of milk at tea-time. Dinah, my dear! I wish you were down here with me! There are no mice in the air, I'm afraid, but you might catch a bat, and that's very like a mouse, you know. But do cats eat bats, I wonder?" And here Alice began to get rather sleepy, and went on saying to herself, in a dreamy sort of way, "Do cats eat bats? Do cats eat bats?" and sometimes, "Do bats eat cats?" for, you see, as she couldn't answer either question, it didn't much matter which way she put it. She felt that she was dozing off, and had just begun to dream that she was walking hand in hand with Dinah, and was saying to her, very earnestly, "Now, Dinah, tell me the truth: did you ever eat a bat?" when suddenly, thump! thump! down she came upon a heap of sticks and dry leaves, and the fall was over.

Alice was not a bit hurt, and she jumped up on to her feet in a moment: she looked up, but it was all dark overhead: before her was another long passage, and the White Rabbit was still in sight, hurrying down it. There was not a moment to be lost: away went Alice like the wind, and was just in time to hear it say, as it turned a corner, "Oh my ears and whiskers, how late it's getting!" She was close behind it when she turned the corner, but the Rabbit was no longer to be seen: she found herself in a long, low hall, which was lit up by a row of lamps hanging from the roof.

There were doors all round the hall, but they were all locked, and when Alice had been all the way down one side and up the other, trying every door, she walked sadly down the middle, wondering how she was ever to get out again.

passage: hallway; corridor

Suddenly she came upon a little three-legged table, all made of solid glass: there was nothing on it but a tiny golden key, and Alice's first idea was that this might belong to one of the doors of the hall; but alas! either the locks were too large, or the key was too small, but at any rate it would not open any of them. However, on the second time round, she came upon a low curtain she had not noticed before, and behind it was a little door about fifteen inches high: she tried the little golden key in the lock, and to her great delight it fit!

Alice opened the door and found that it led into a small passage, not much larger than a rat-hole: she knelt down and looked along the passage into the loveliest garden you ever saw. How she longed to get out of that dark hall, and wander about among those beds of bright flowers and those cool fountains, but she could not even get her head through the doorway; "and even if my head *would* go through," thought poor Alice, "it would be of very little use without my shoulders. Oh, how I wish I could shut up like a telescope! I think I could, if I only knew how to begin." For, you see, so many out-of-the-way things had happened lately, that Alice had begun to think that very few things indeed were really impossible.

There seemed to be no use in waiting by the little door, so she went back to the table, half hoping she might find another key on it, or at any rate a book of rules for shutting people up like telescopes: this time she found a little bottle on it ("Which certainly was not here before," said Alice), and tied round the neck of the bottle was a paper label, with the words "DRINK ME" beautifully printed on it in large letters.

It was all very well to say "Drink me," but the wise little Alice was not going to do *that* in a hurry. "No, I'll look first," she said, "and see whether it's marked 'poison' or not"; for she had read several nice little stories about children who had got burned, and eaten up by wild beasts, and other unpleasant things, all because they *would* not remember the simple rules their friends had taught them: such as, that a red-hot poker will burn you if you hold it too long; and that, if you cut your finger very deeply with a knife, it usually bleeds; and she had never forgotten that, if you drink much from a bottle marked "poison," it is almost certain to disagree with you, sooner or later.

However, this bottle was *not* marked "poison," so Alice ventured to taste it, and, finding it very nice (it had, in fact, a sort of mixed flavor of cherry-tart, custard, pineapple, roast turkey, toffy, and hot buttered toast), she very soon finished it off.

poker: a metal rod used for stirring up a fire
ventured: tried; dared
toffy: (also spelled *toffee*) a kind of candy

* * * * *

"What a curious feeling!" said Alice. "I must be shutting up like a telescope!"

And so it was indeed: she was now only ten inches high, and her face brightened up at the thought that she was now the right size for going through the little door into that lovely garden. First, however, she waited for a few minutes to see if she was going to shrink any further: she felt a little nervous about this; "for it might end, you know," said Alice to herself, "in my going out altogether, like a candle. I wonder what I should be like then?" And she tried to fancy what the flame of a candle looks like after the candle is blown out, for she could not remember ever having seen such a thing.

After a while, finding that nothing more happened, she decided on going into the garden at once; but, alas for poor Alice! when she got to the door, she found she had forgotten the little golden key, and when she went back to the table for it, she found she could not possibly reach it: she could see it quite plainly through the glass, and she tried her best to climb up one of the legs of the table, but it was too slippery; and when she had tired herself out with trying, the poor little thing sat down and cried.

"Come, there's no use in crying like that!" said Alice to herself, rather sharply. "I advise you to leave off this minute!" She generally gave herself very good advice (though she very seldom followed it), and sometimes she scolded herself so severely as to bring tears into her eyes; and once she remembered trying to box her own ears for having cheated herself in a game of croquet she

severely: harshly, sternly
croquet: a game played with a ball, a mallet, and wickets, in which players
    strike the ball with the mallet and aim it through the wickets

was playing against herself, for this curious child was very fond of pretending to be two people. "But it's no use now," thought poor Alice, "to pretend to be two people! Why, there's hardly enough of me left to make one respectable person!"

Soon her eye fell on a little glass box that was lying under the table: she opened it, and found in it a very small cake, on which the words "EAT ME" were beautifully marked in currants. "Well, I'll eat it," said Alice, "and if it makes me grow larger, I can reach the key; and if it makes me grow smaller, I can creep under the door: so either way I'll get into the garden, and I don't care which happens!"

She ate a little bit, and said anxiously to herself, "Which way? Which way?" holding her hand on the top of her head to feel which way it was growing; and she was quite surprised to find that she remained the same size. To be sure, this is what generally happens when one eats cake; but Alice had got so much into the way of expecting nothing but out-of-the-way things to happen, that it seemed quite dull and stupid for life to go on in the common way.

So she set to work, and very soon finished off the cake.

---

currants: dried fruits similar to raisins
anxiously: in a worried way

"Curiouser and curiouser!" cried Alice (she was so much surprised, that for the moment she quite forgot how to speak good English); "now I'm opening out like the largest telescope that ever was! Good-bye, feet!" (For when she looked down at her feet, they seemed to be almost out of

sight, they were getting so far off). "Oh, my poor little feet, I wonder who will put on your shoes and stockings for you now, dears? I'm sure I shan't be able! I shall be a great deal too far off to trouble myself about you: you must manage the best way you can—but I must be kind to them," thought Alice, "or perhaps they won't walk the way I want to go! Let me see. I'll give them a new pair of boots every Christmas."

And she went on planning to herself how she would manage it. "They must go by the carrier," she thought; "and how funny it'll seem, sending presents to one's own feet! And how odd the directions will look!

> *Alice's Right Foot, Esq.,*
>> *Hearthrug,*
>>> *near the Fender,*
>>>> *(with Alice's love).*

Oh dear, what nonsense I'm talking!"

Just at this moment her head struck against the roof of the hall: in fact she was now rather more than nine feet high, and she at once took up the little golden key and hurried off to the garden door.

Poor Alice! It was as much as she could do, lying down on one side, to look through into the garden with one eye; but to get through was more hopeless than ever: she sat down and began to cry again.

"You ought to be ashamed of yourself," said Alice, "a great girl like you" (she might well say this), "to go on crying in this way! Stop this moment, I tell you!"

But she went on all the same, shedding gallons of tears, until there was a large pool all round her, about four inches deep, and reaching half down the hall.

After a time she heard a little pattering of feet in the distance, and she hastily dried her eyes to see what was coming. It was the White Rabbit returning, splendidly dressed, with a pair of white kid-gloves in one hand and a large fan in the other: he came trotting along in a great hurry, muttering to himself, as he came, "Oh! the Duchess, the Duchess! Oh! *won't* she be savage if I've kept her waiting!"

Alice felt so desperate that she was ready to ask help of anyone: so, when the Rabbit came near her, she began, in a

---

hearthrug: a rug in front of a fireplace
fender: a screen in front of a fireplace
pattering: small, hurried sounds
kid-gloves: gloves made with the skin of a young goat
savage: fierce; ferocious

low, timid voice, "If you please, Sir—" The Rabbit started violently, dropped the white kid-gloves and the fan, and scurried away into the darkness as hard as he could go.

Alice took up the fan and gloves, and, as the hall was very hot, she kept fanning herself all the time she went on talking. "Dear, dear! How queer everything is today! And yesterday things went on just as usual. I wonder if I've been changed in the night? Let me think: was I the same when I got up this morning? I almost think I can remember feeling a little different. But if I'm not the same, the next question is, 'Who in the world am I?' Ah, *that's* the great puzzle!" And she began thinking over all the children she knew that were of the same age as herself, to see if she could have been changed for any of them.

"I'm sure I'm not Ada," she said, "for her hair goes in such long ringlets, and mine doesn't go in ringlets at all; and I'm sure I can't be Mabel, for I know all sorts of things, and she, oh, she knows such a very little! Besides, *she's* she, and *I'm* I, and—oh dear, how puzzling it all is! I'll try if I know all the things I used to know. Let me see: four times five is

scurried: moved quickly
ringlets: curls

twelve, and four times six is thirteen, and four times seven is—oh dear! I shall never get to twenty at that rate! However, the Multiplication Table doesn't signify: let's try Geography. London is the capital of Paris, and Paris is the capital of Rome, and Rome—no, that's all wrong, I'm certain! I must have been changed for Mabel! I'll try and say 'How doth the little—,'" and she crossed her hands on her lap, as if she were saying lessons, and began to repeat it, but her voice sounded hoarse and strange, and the words did not come the same as they used to do:

> "How doth the little crocodile
>   Improve his shining tail,
> And pour the waters of the Nile
>   On every golden scale!
>
> "How cheerfully he seems to grin,
>   How neatly spreads his claws,
> And welcomes little fishes in
>   With gently smiling jaws!"

"I'm sure those are not the right words," said poor Alice, and her eyes filled with tears again as she went on, "I must be Mabel after all, and I shall have to go and live in that poky little house, and have next to no toys to play with, and oh, ever so many lessons to learn! No, I've made up my mind about it: if I'm Mabel, I'll stay down here! It'll be no use their putting their heads down and saying, 'Come up again, dear!' I shall only look up and say, 'Who am I, then? Tell me that first, and then, if I like being that person, I'll come up: if not, I'll stay down here till I am somebody else'—but, oh dear!"

---

poky: very small

cried Alice, with a sudden burst of tears, "I do wish they *would* put their heads down! I am so very tired of being all alone here!"

As she said this she looked down at her hands, and was surprised to see that she had put on one of the Rabbit's little white kid-gloves while she was talking.

"How *can* I have done that?" she thought. "I must be growing small again." She got up and went to the table to measure herself by it, and found that, as nearly as she could guess, she was now about two feet high, and was going on shrinking rapidly: she soon found out that the cause of this was the fan she was holding, and she dropped it hastily, just in time to save herself from shrinking away altogether.

"That *was* a narrow escape!" said Alice, a good deal frightened at the sudden change, but very glad to find herself still in existence. "And now for the garden!" And she ran with all speed back to the little door; but, alas! the little door was shut again, and the little golden key was lying on the glass table as before, "and things are worse than ever," thought the poor child, "for I never was so small as this before, never! And I declare it's too bad, that it is!"

As she said these words her foot slipped, and in another moment, splash! she was up to her chin in salt water. Her first idea was that she had somehow fallen into the sea, "and in that case I can go back by railway," she said to herself. (Alice had been to the seaside once in her life, and had come to the general conclusion that, wherever you go to on the English coast, you find a number of bathing machines in the sea, some children digging in the sand with wooden spades, then a row of lodging-houses, and behind them a railway station.)

---

bathing machines: a wheeled canvas huts that carried swimmers into the
    sea so that they could swim in privacy

However, she soon made out that she was in the pool of tears which she had wept when she was nine feet high.

"I wish I hadn't cried so much!" said Alice, as she swam about, trying to find her way out. "I shall be punished for it now, I suppose, by being drowned in my own tears! That *will* be a queer thing, to be sure! However, everything is queer today."

[Alice continues to have a strange day. She sees the White Rabbit again and follows him to his house. There, she drinks from a bottle, and the liquid makes her grow so large that her head presses against the ceiling! But then a bite of cake makes her shrink to a tiny size, just inches tall. She runs from the house into a thick wood, where she is almost trampled by a playful puppy. After escaping from the puppy, Alice continues on her way, worrying about how to get back to her normal size.]

"Oh dear! I'd nearly forgotten that I've got to grow up again! Let me see—how *is* it to be managed? I suppose I ought to eat or drink something or other; but the great question is, 'What?'"

The great question certainly was "What?" Alice looked all round her at the flowers and the blades of grass, but she could not see anything that looked like the right thing to eat or drink under the circumstances. There was a large mushroom growing near her, about the same height as herself; and, when she had looked under it, and on both sides of it, and behind it, it occurred to her that she might as well look and see what was on the top of it.

---

trampled: heavily stepped on to bruise or cause injury

She stretched herself up on tiptoe, and peeped over the edge of the mushroom, and her eyes immediately met those of a large blue caterpillar, that was sitting on the top, with his arms folded, quietly smoking a long hookah, and taking not the smallest notice of her or of anything else.

ADVICE FROM A CATERPILLAR

The Caterpillar and Alice looked at each other for some time in silence: at last the Caterpillar took the hookah out of its mouth, and addressed her in a languid, sleepy voice.

"Who are *you?*" said the Caterpillar.

This was not an encouraging opening for a conversation. Alice replied, rather shyly, "I—I hardly know, Sir, just at present—at least I know who I *was* when I got up this morning, but I think I must have changed several times since then."

"What do you mean by that?" said the Caterpillar, sternly. "Explain yourself!"

"I can't explain *myself,* I'm afraid, Sir," said Alice, "because I'm not myself, you see."

"I don't see," said the Caterpillar.

"I'm afraid I can't put it more clearly," Alice replied, very politely, "for I can't understand it myself, to begin with; and being so many different sizes in a day is very confusing."

"It isn't," said the Caterpillar.

"Well, perhaps you haven't found it so yet," said Alice; "but when you have to turn into a chrysalis—you will some day,

---

hookah: a water pipe
languid: without energy; sluggish
chrysalis: a stage in the development of a butterfly or moth, in which the
    insect is enclosed in a cocoon

you know—and then after that into a butterfly, I should think
you'll feel it a little queer, won't you?"

"Not a bit," said the Caterpillar.

"Well, perhaps *your* feelings may be different," said Alice:
"all I know is, it would feel very queer to *me*."

"You!" said the Caterpillar contemptuously. "Who
are *you?*"

Which brought them back again to the beginning of
the conversation.

---

contemptuously: scornfully; disrespectfully

Alice felt a little irritated at the Caterpillar's making such *very* short remarks, and she drew herself up and said, very gravely, "I think you ought to tell me who *you* are, first."

"Why?" said the Caterpillar.

Here was another puzzling question; and, as Alice could not think of any good reason, and the Caterpillar seemed to be in a very unpleasant state of mind, she turned away.

"Come back!" the Caterpillar called after her. "I've something important to say!"

This sounded promising, certainly. Alice turned and came back again.

"Keep your temper," said the Caterpillar.

"Is that all?" said Alice, swallowing down her anger as well as she could.

"No," said the Caterpillar.

Alice thought she might as well wait, as she had nothing else to do, and perhaps after all it might tell her something worth hearing. For some minutes it puffed away without speaking; but at last it unfolded its arms, took the hookah out of its mouth again, and said, "So you think you're changed, do you?"

"I'm afraid I am, Sir," said Alice. "I can't remember things as I used—and I don't keep the same size for ten minutes together!"

"Can't remember *what* things?" said the Caterpillar.

"Well, I've tried to say, 'How doth the little busy bee,' but it all came different!" Alice replied in a very melancholy voice.

"Repeat, *'You are old, Father William,'*" said the Caterpillar.

---

melancholy: very sad; gloomy

Alice folded her hands, and began:

"*You are old, Father William,*" *the young man said,*
    "*And your hair has become very white;*
And yet you incessantly stand on your head —
    Do you think, at your age, it is right?"

"*In my youth,*" *Father William replied to his son,*
    "*I feared it might injure the brain;*
But, now that I'm perfectly sure I have none,
    Why, I do it again and again."

"*You are old,*" *said the youth,* "*as I mentioned before,*
    And have grown most uncommonly fat;
Yet you turned a back-somersault in at the door —
    Pray, what is the reason of that?"

---

incessantly: constantly; without stopping

"In my youth," said the sage, as he shook his gray locks,
    "I kept all my limbs very supple
By the use of this ointment—one shilling the box—
    Allow me to sell you a couple."

"You are old," said the youth, "and your jaws are too weak
    For anything tougher than suet;
Yet you finished the goose, with the bones and the beak—
    Pray, how did you manage to do it?"

sage: a wise person
locks: strands of hair
supple: flexible; able to bend and twist easily
shilling: an English coin
suet: hard fat from a cow or sheep

"In my youth," said his father, "I took to the law,
    And argued each case with my wife;
And the muscular strength, which it gave to my jaw,
    Has lasted the rest of my life."

"You are old," said the youth, "one would hardly suppose
    That your eye was as steady as ever;
Yet you balanced an eel on the end of your nose—
    What made you so awfully clever?"

"I have answered three questions, and that is enough,"
    Said his father; "don't give yourself airs!
Do you think I can listen all day to such stuff?
    Be off, or I'll kick you downstairs!"

"That is not said right," said the Caterpillar.

"Not *quite* right, I'm afraid," said Alice, timidly: "some of the words have got altered."

"It is wrong from beginning to end," said the Caterpillar, decidedly, and there was silence for some minutes.

The Caterpillar was the first to speak.

"What size do you want to be?" it asked.

"Oh, I'm not particular as to size," Alice hastily replied; "only one doesn't like changing so often, you know."

"I *don't* know," said the Caterpillar.

Alice said nothing: she had never been so much contradicted in all her life before, and she felt that she was losing her temper.

"Are you content now?" said the Caterpillar.

"Well, I should like to be a *little* larger, Sir, if you wouldn't mind," said Alice: "three inches is such a wretched height to be."

"It is a very good height indeed!" said the Caterpillar angrily, rearing itself upright as it spoke (it was exactly three inches high).

"But I'm not used to it!" pleaded poor Alice in a piteous tone. And she thought to herself, "I wish the creature wouldn't be so easily offended!"

"You'll get used to it in time," said the Caterpillar; and it put the hookah into its mouth, and began smoking again.

This time Alice waited patiently until it chose to speak again. In a minute or two the Caterpillar took the hookah out of its mouth, and yawned once or twice, and shook itself. Then

---

timidly: shyly
altered: changed
contradicted: argued against
piteous: worthy of pity or compassion

it got down off the mushroom, and crawled away into the grass, merely remarking, as it went, "One side will make you grow taller, and the other side will make you grow shorter."

"One side of *what?* The other side of *what?*" thought Alice to herself.

"Of the mushroom," said the Caterpillar, just as if she had asked it aloud; and in another moment it was out of sight.

Alice remained looking thoughtfully at the mushroom for a minute, trying to make out which were the two sides of it; and, as it was perfectly round, she found this a very difficult question. However, at last she stretched her arms round it as far as they would go, and broke off a bit of the edge with each hand.

"And now which is which?" she said to herself, and nibbled a little of the right-hand bit to try the effect.

The next moment she felt a violent blow underneath her chin: it had struck her foot!

She was a good deal frightened by this very sudden change, but she felt that there was no time to be lost, as she was shrinking rapidly: so she set to work at once to eat some of the other bit. Her chin was pressed so closely against her foot, that there was hardly room to open her mouth; but she did it at last, and managed to swallow a morsel of the left-hand bit.

[After a good deal of violent shrinking down and shooting up, Alice manages, by very carefully nibbling first at one side of the mush-room and then at the other, to succeed in restoring herself to her usual height. She proceeds on her way and continues to have extraordinary adventures. She comes across a tiny house and uses the mushroom to shrink herself to nine inches. In this house she

---

morsel: a tiny piece

meets a very cross Duchess. The Duchess has a large cat — a Cheshire cat — that grins from ear to ear. The Duchess is holding a crying baby. When the Duchess suddenly leaves to go play croquet with the Queen, she flings the baby at Alice. When Alice takes the baby into her arms, she hears a grunting sound.]

"Don't grunt," said Alice; "that's not at all a proper way of expressing yourself."

The baby grunted again, and Alice looked very anxiously into its face to see what was the matter with it. There could be no doubt that it had a very turn-up nose, much more like a snout than a real nose: also its eyes were getting extremely small for a baby: altogether Alice did not like the look of the thing at all. "But perhaps it was only sobbing," she thought, and looked into its eyes again, to see if there were any tears.

No, there were no tears. "If you're going to turn into a pig, my dear" said Alice, seriously, "I'll have nothing more to do with you. Mind now!" The poor little thing sobbed again (or grunted, it was impossible to say which), and they went on for some while in silence.

Alice was just beginning to think to herself, "Now, what am I to do with this creature when I get it home?" when it grunted again, so violently, that she looked down into its face in some alarm. This time there could be no mistake about it: it was neither more nor less than a pig, and she felt that it would be quite absurd for her to carry it any further.

So she set the little creature down, and felt quite relieved to see it trot away quietly into the wood. "If it had grown up," she said to herself, "it would have made a dreadfully ugly child: but it makes rather a handsome pig, I think." And she began thinking over other children she knew, who might do very well as pigs, and was just saying to herself, "if one

only knew the right way to change them—" when she was a little startled by seeing the Cheshire Cat sitting on a bough of a tree a few yards off.

The Cat only grinned when it saw Alice. It looked good-natured, she thought: still it had very long claws and a great many teeth, so she felt that it ought to be treated with respect.

"Cheshire Puss," she began, rather timidly, as she did not at all know whether it would like the name: however, it only grinned a little wider. "Come, it's pleased so far," thought Alice, and she went on: "Would you tell me, please, which way I ought to go from here?"

"That depends a good deal on where you want to get to," said the Cat.

"I don't much care where—," said Alice.

"Then it doesn't matter which way you go," said the Cat.

"—so long as I get *somewhere*," Alice added as an explanation.

"Oh, you're sure to do that," said the Cat, "if you only walk long enough."

Alice felt that this could not be denied, so she tried another question. "What sort of people live about here?"

bough: a branch

"In *that* direction," the Cat said, waving its right paw round, "lives a Hatter: and in *that* direction," waving the other paw, "lives a March Hare. Visit either you like: they're both mad."

"But I don't want to go among mad people," Alice remarked.

"Oh, you can't help that," said the Cat: "we're all mad here. I'm mad. You're mad."

"How do you know I'm mad?" said Alice.

"You must be," said the Cat, "or you wouldn't have come here."

Alice didn't think that proved it at all; however, she went on: "And how do you know that you're mad?"

"To begin with," said the Cat, "a dog's not mad. You grant that?"

"I suppose so," said Alice.

"Well, then," the Cat went on, "you see a dog growls when it's angry, and wags its tail when it's pleased. Now *I* growl when I'm pleased, and wag my tail when I'm angry. Therefore I'm mad."

"*I* call it purring, not growling," said Alice.

"Call it what you like," said the Cat. "Do you play croquet with the Queen today?"

"I should like it very much," said Alice, "but I haven't been invited yet."

"You'll see me there," said the Cat, and vanished.

Alice was not much surprised at this, she was getting so well used to queer things happening. While she was still looking at the place where it had been, it suddenly appeared again.

"By the by, what became of the baby?" said the Cat. "I'd nearly forgotten to ask."

---

mad: insane

"It turned into a pig," Alice answered very quietly, just is if the Cat had come back in a natural way.

"I thought it would," said the Cat, and vanished again.

Alice waited a little, half expecting to see it again, but it did not appear, and after a minute or two she walked on in the direction in which the March Hare was said to live. "I've seen hatters before," she said to herself: "the March Hare will be much the most interesting, and perhaps, as this is May, it won't be raving mad—at least not so mad as it was in March." As she said this, she looked up, and there was the Cat again sitting on a branch of a tree.

"Did you say 'pig,' or 'fig'?" said the Cat.

"I said 'pig'," replied Alice; "and I wish you wouldn't keep appearing and vanishing so suddenly: you make one quite giddy!"

"All right," said the Cat; and this time it vanished quite slowly, beginning with the end of the tail, and ending with the grin, which remained some time after the rest of it had gone.

"Well! I've often seen a cat without a grin," thought Alice; "but a grin without a cat! It's the most curious thing I ever saw in all my life!"

She had not gone much farther before she came in sight of the house of the March Hare: she thought it must be the right house, because the chimneys were shaped like ears and the roof was thatched with fur. It was so large a house, that she did not like to go nearer till she had nibbled some more of the left-hand bit of mushroom, and raised herself to about two feet high: even then she walked up toward it rather timidly, saying to herself, "Suppose it should be raving mad after all! I almost wish I'd gone to see the Hatter instead!"

giddy: dizzy

A Mad Tea-Party

There was a table set out under a tree in front of the house, and the March Hare and the Hatter were having tea at it. A Dormouse was sitting between them, fast asleep, and the other two were using it as a cushion, resting their elbows on it, and talking over its head. "Very uncomfortable for the Dormouse," thought Alice; "only as it's asleep, I suppose it doesn't mind."

The table was a large one, but the three were all crowded together at one corner of it. "No room! No room!" they cried out when they saw Alice coming.

"There's *plenty* of room!" said Alice indignantly, and she sat down in a large armchair at one end of the table.

"Have some wine," the March Hare said in an encouraging tone.

Alice looked all round the table, but there was nothing on it but tea. "I don't see any wine," she remarked.

"There isn't any," said the March Hare.

"Then it wasn't very civil of you to offer it," said Alice angrily.

"It wasn't very civil of you to sit down without being invited," said the March Hare.

"I didn't know it was *your* table," said Alice: "it's laid for a great many more than three."

"Your hair wants cutting," said the Hatter. He had been looking at Alice for some time with great curiosity, and this was his first speech.

Dormouse: a rodent that is somewhat like a mouse and a squirrel
indignantly: with anger in response to something seen as unjust or mean
civil: polite; courteous

"You should learn not to make personal remarks," Alice said with some severity: "it's very rude."

The Hatter opened his eyes very wide on hearing this; but all he *said* was, "Why is a raven like a writing desk?"

"Come, we shall have some fun now!" thought Alice. "I'm glad they've begun asking riddles—I believe I can guess that," she added, aloud.

"Do you mean that you think you can find out the answer to it?" said the March Hare.

"Exactly so," said Alice.

"Then you should say what you mean," the March Hare went on.

"I do," Alice hastily replied; "at least—at least I mean what I say—that's the same thing, you know."

"Not the same thing a bit!" said the Hatter. "Why, you might just as well say that 'I see what I eat' is the same thing as 'I eat what I see'!"

---

severity: harshness

"You might just as well say," added the March Hare, "that 'I like what I get' is the same thing as 'I get what I like'!"

"You might just as well say," added the Dormouse, which seemed to be talking in its sleep, "that 'I breathe when I sleep' is the same thing as 'I sleep when I breathe'!"

"It is the same thing with you," said the Hatter, and here the conversation dropped, and the party sat silent for a minute, while Alice thought over all she could remember about ravens and writing-desks, which wasn't much.

The Hatter was the first to break the silence. "What day of the month is it?" he said, turning to Alice: he had taken his watch out of his pocket, and was looking at it uneasily, shaking it every now and then, and holding it to his ear.

Alice considered a little, and then said, "The fourth."

"Two days wrong!" sighed the Hatter. "I told you butter wouldn't suit the works!" he added, looking angrily at the March Hare.

"It was the *best* butter," the March Hare meekly replied.

"Yes, but some crumbs must have got in as well," the Hatter grumbled: "you shouldn't have put it in with the bread-knife."

The March Hare took the watch and looked at it gloomily: then he dipped it into his cup of tea, and looked at it again: but he could think of nothing better to say than his first remark, "It was the *best* butter, you know."

Alice had been looking over his shoulder with some curiosity. "What a funny watch!" she remarked. "It tells the day of the month, and doesn't tell what o'clock it is!"

"Why should it?" muttered the Hatter. "Does *your* watch tell you what year it is?"

"Of course not," Alice replied very readily: "but that's because it stays the same year for such a long time together."

"Which is just the case with *mine*," said the Hatter.

Alice felt dreadfully puzzled. The Hatter's remark seemed to her to have no sort of meaning in it, and yet it was certainly English. "I don't quite understand you," she said, as politely as she could.

"The Dormouse is asleep again," said the Hatter, and he poured a little hot tea upon its nose.

The Dormouse shook its head impatiently, and said, without opening its eyes, "Of course, of course: just what I was going to remark myself."

"Have you guessed the riddle yet?" the Hatter said, turning to Alice again.

"No, I give it up," Alice replied. "What's the answer?"

"I haven't the slightest idea," said the Hatter.

"Nor I," said the March Hare.

Alice sighed wearily. "I think you might do something better with the time," she said, "than wasting it in asking riddles that have no answers."

"If you knew Time as well as I do," said the Hatter, "you wouldn't talk about wasting it. It's him."

"I don't know what you mean," said Alice.

"Of course you don't!" the Hatter said, tossing his head contemptuously. "I dare say you never even spoke to Time!"

"Perhaps not," Alice cautiously replied; "but I know I have to beat time when I learn music."

"Ah! That accounts for it," said the Hatter. "He won't stand beating. Now, if you only kept on good terms with him, he'd do almost anything you liked with the clock. For instance, suppose it were nine o'clock in the morning, just time to begin lessons: you'd only have to whisper a hint to Time, and round goes the clock in a twinkling! Half-past one, time for dinner!"

twinkling: an instant or moment

("I only wish it was," the March Hare said to itself in a whisper.)

"That would be grand, certainly," said Alice thoughtfully; "but then—I shouldn't be hungry for it, you know."

"Not at first, perhaps," said the Hatter: "but you could keep it to half-past one as long as you liked."

"Is that the way *you* manage?" Alice asked.

The Hatter shook his head mournfully. "Not I!" he replied. "We quarreled last March— just before he went mad, you know—" (pointing with his teaspoon at the March Hare), "—it was at the great concert given by the Queen of Hearts, and I had to sing:

> '*Twinkle, twinkle, little bat!*
> *How I wonder what you're at!*'

You know the song, perhaps?"

"I've heard something like it," said Alice.

"It goes on, you know," the Hatter continued, "in this way:—

> '*Up above the world you fly,*
> *Like a tea-tray in the sky.*
> *Twinkle, twinkle—*'"

---

mournfully: very sadly

Here the Dormouse shook itself, and began singing in its sleep, *"Twinkle, twinkle, twinkle, twinkle—"* and went on so long that they had to pinch it to make it stop.

"Well, I'd hardly finished the first verse," said the Hatter, "when the Queen bawled out, 'He's murdering the time! Off with his head!'"

"How dreadfully savage!" exclaimed Alice.

"And ever since that," the Hatter went on in a mournful tone, "he won't do a thing I ask! It's always six o'clock now."

A bright idea came into Alice's head. "Is that the reason so many tea-things are put out here?" she asked.

"Yes, that's it," said the Hatter with a sigh: "it's always tea-time, and we've no time to wash the things between whiles."

"Then you keep moving round, I suppose?" said Alice.

"Exactly so," said the Hatter: "as the things get used up."

"But what happens when you come to the beginning again?" Alice ventured to ask.

"Suppose we change the subject," the March Hare interrupted, yawning. "I'm getting tired of this. I vote the young lady tells us a story."

"I'm afraid I don't know one," said Alice, rather alarmed at the proposal.

"Then the Dormouse shall!" they both cried. "Wake up, Dormouse!" And they pinched it on both sides at once.

The Dormouse slowly opened its eyes. "I wasn't asleep," it said in a hoarse, feeble voice, "I heard every word you fellows were saying."

"Tell us a story!" said the March Hare.

"Yes, please do!" pleaded Alice.

---

feeble: very weak

"And be quick about it," added the Hatter, "or you'll be asleep again before it's done."

"Once upon a time there were three little sisters," the Dormouse began in a great hurry; "and their names were Elsie, Lacie, and Tillie; and they lived at the bottom of a well—"

"What did they live on?" said Alice, who always took a great interest in questions of eating and drinking.

"They lived on treacle," said the Dormouse, after thinking a minute or two.

"They couldn't have done that, you know," Alice gently remarked. "They'd have been ill."

"So they were," said the Dormouse; "very ill."

Alice tried a little to fancy to herself what such an extraordinary way of living would be like, but it puzzled her too much: so she went on: "But why did they live at the bottom of a well?"

"Take some more tea," the March Hare said to Alice, very earnestly.

"I've had nothing yet," Alice replied in an offended tone: "so I can't take more."

"You mean you can't take *less*," said the Hatter: "it's very easy to take *more* than nothing."

"Nobody asked *your* opinion," said Alice.

"Who's making personal remarks now?" the Hatter asked triumphantly.

Alice did not quite know what to say to this: so she helped herself to some tea and bread-and-butter, and then turned to the Dormouse, and repeated her question. "Why did they live at the bottom of a well?"

---

treacle: molasses; a thick sweet syrup made from sugar cane

The Dormouse again took a minute or two to think about it, and then said, "It was a treacle-well."

"There's no such thing!" Alice was beginning very angrily, but the Hatter and the March Hare went, "Sh! Sh!" and the Dormouse sulkily remarked, "If you can't be civil, you'd better finish the story for yourself."

"No, please go on!" Alice said very humbly, "I won't interrupt you again. I dare say there may be *one*."

"One, indeed!" said the Dormouse indignantly. However, he consented to go on. "And so these three little sisters—they were learning to draw, you know—"

"What did they draw?" said Alice, quite forgetting her promise.

"Treacle," said the Dormouse, without considering at all, this time.

"I want a clean cup," interrupted the Hatter: "let's all move one place on."

He moved on as he spoke, and the Dormouse followed him: the March Hare moved into the Dormouse's place, and Alice rather unwillingly took the place of the March Hare. The Hatter was the only one who got any advantage from the change; and Alice was a good deal worse off than before, as the March Hare had just upset the milk-jug into his plate.

Alice did not wish to offend the Dormouse again, so she began very cautiously: "But I don't understand. Where did they draw the treacle from?"

"You can draw water out of a water-well," said the Hatter; "so I should think you could draw treacle out of a treacle-well—eh, stupid?"

---

sulkily: in a sullen, gloomy, moody way
consented: agreed

"But they were *in* the well," Alice said to the Dormouse, not choosing to notice this last remark.

"Of course they were," said the Dormouse: "well in."

This answer so confused poor Alice, that she let the Dormouse go on for some time without interrupting it.

"They were learning to draw," the Dormouse went on, yawning and rubbing its eyes, for it was getting very sleepy; "and they drew all manner of things—everything that begins with an *M*—"

"Why with an *M*?" said Alice.

"Why not?" said the March Hare.

Alice was silent.

The Dormouse had closed its eyes by this time, and was going off into a doze; but, on being pinched by the Hatter, it woke up again with a little shriek, and went on: "—that begins with an M, such as mouse-traps, and the moon, and memory, and muchness—you know you say things are 'much of a muchness'—did you ever see such a thing as a drawing of a muchness?"

"Really, now you ask me," said Alice, very much confused, "I don't think—"

"Then you shouldn't talk," said the Hatter.

This piece of rudeness was more than Alice could bear: she got up in great disgust, and walked off: the Dormouse fell asleep instantly, and neither of the others took the least notice of her going, though she looked back once or twice, half hoping that they would call after her: the last time she saw them, they were trying to put the Dormouse into the teapot.

"At any rate I'll never go *there* again!" said Alice, as she picked her way through the wood. "It's the stupidest tea-party I ever was at in all my life!"

Just as she said this, she noticed that one of the trees had a door leading right into it. "That's very curious!" she thought. "But everything's curious today. I think I may as well go in at once." And in she went.

Once more she found herself in the long hall, and close to the little glass table. "Now, I'll manage better this time," she said to herself, and began by taking the little golden key, and unlocking the door that led into the garden. Then she set to work nibbling at the mushroom (she had kept a piece of it in her pocket) till she was about a foot high: then she walked down the little passage: and *then*—she found herself at last in the beautiful garden among the bright flower-beds and the cool fountains.

[Now that she has made her way to the beautiful garden, will all go well for Alice? Ah, this is Wonderland! Many more adventures are in store for her, which you can enjoy by reading the rest of Alice's Adventures in Wonderland.*]*

THE WALRUS AND THE CARPENTER

from Through the Looking-Glass
and What Alice Found There
by Lewis Carroll

The sun was shining on the sea,
    Shining with all his might:
He did his very best to make
    The billows smooth and bright—
And this was odd, because it was
    The middle of the night.

The moon was shining sulkily,
    Because she thought the sun
Had got no business to be there
    After the day was done—
"It's very rude of him," she said,
    "To come and spoil the fun!"

The sea was wet as wet could be,
    The sands were dry as dry.
You could not see a cloud, because
    No cloud was in the sky:
No birds were flying overhead—
    There were no birds to fly.

---

billows: large waves

The Walrus and the Carpenter
　　Were walking close at hand;
They wept like anything to see
　　Such quantities of sand:
"If this were only cleared away,"
　　They said, "it *would* be grand!"

"If seven maids with seven mops
　　Swept it for half a year,
Do you suppose," the Walrus said,
　　"That they could get it clear?"
"I doubt it," said the Carpenter,
　　And shed a bitter tear.

"O, Oysters, come and walk with us!"
　　The Walrus did beseech.
"A pleasant talk, a pleasant walk,
　　Along the briny beach:
We cannot do with more than four,
　　To give a hand to each."

---

beseech: to beg or plead
briny: salty (from brine, the salty seawater)

The eldest Oyster looked at him,
  But never a word he said;
The eldest Oyster winked his eye,
  And shook his heavy head—
Meaning to say he did not choose
  To leave the oyster-bed.

But four young Oysters hurried up,
  All eager for the treat:
Their coats were brushed, their faces washed,
  Their shoes were clean and neat—
And this was odd, because, you know,
  They hadn't any feet.

Four other Oysters followed them,
    And yet another four;
And thick and fast they came at last,
    And more, and more, and more—
All hopping through the frothy waves,
    And scrambling to the shore.

The Walrus and the Carpenter
    Walked on a mile or so,
And then they rested on a rock
    Conveniently low:
And all the little Oysters stood
    And waited in a row.

"The time has come," the Walrus said,
    "To talk of many things:
Of shoes—and ships—and sealing-wax—
    Of cabbages—and kings—
And why the sea is boiling hot—
    And whether pigs have wings."

"But wait a bit," the Oysters cried,
    "Before we have our chat;
For some of us are out of breath,
    And all of us are fat!"
"No hurry!" said the Carpenter.
    They thanked him much for that.

---

frothy: foamy; bubby
sealing-wax: substance used to close or seal something, such as
    an envelope

"A loaf of bread," the Walrus said,
  "Is what we chiefly need:
Pepper and vinegar besides
  Are very good indeed—
Now, if you're ready, Oysters dear,
  We can begin to feed."

"But not on us!" the Oysters cried,
  Turning a little blue.
"After such kindness, that would be
  A dismal thing to do!"
"The night is fine," the Walrus said
  "Do you admire the view?

"It was so kind of you to come!
  And you are very nice!"
The Carpenter said nothing but
  "Cut us another slice:
I wish you were not quite so deaf—
  I've had to ask you twice!"

"It seems a shame," the Walrus said,
  "To play them such a trick,
After we've brought them out so far,
  And made them trot so quick!"
The Carpenter said nothing but
  "The butter's spread too thick!"

---

dismal: especially bad; causing great discouragement or fear

"I weep for you," the Walrus said:
    "I deeply sympathize."
With sobs and tears he sorted out
    Those of the largest size,
Holding his pocket handkerchief
    Before his streaming eyes.

"O Oysters," said the Carpenter,
    "You've had a pleasant run!
Shall we be trotting home again?
    But answer came there none—
And this was scarcely odd, because
    They'd eaten every one.

---

sympathize: to share the feelings or sorrows of others

A SELECTION OF LIMERICKS
by Edward Lear

There was an Old Man in a tree,
Who was horribly bored by a Bee;
   When they said, "Does it buzz?"
   He replied, "Yes, it does!
It's a regular brute of a Bee!"

There was an Old Person of Ware,
Who rode on the back of a bear.
   When they asked, "Does it trot?"
   He said, "Certainly *not!*
He's a Moppsikon Floppsikon bear!"

There was an Old Man of Dumbree
Who taught little owls to drink tea;
   For he said, "To eat mice
   Is not proper or nice,"
That amiable Man of Dumbree.

There was an Old Man who, when little,
Fell casually into a kettle;
   But growing too stout
   He could never get out—
So he passed al his life in that kettle!

---

brute: a beast; someone fierce and cruel
amiable: friendly
stout: fat

There was an Old Man who said, "Hush!
I perceive a young bird in this bush!"
    When they said, "Is it small?"
    He replied, "Not at all!
It is ten times as big as the bush!"

There was an Old Person whose habits
Induced him to feed upon rabbits;
    When he'd eaten eighteen,
    He turned perfectly green,
Upon which he relinquished those habits.

There was an Old Man with a beard,
Who said, "It is just as I feared!—
    Two Owls and a Hen,
    Four Larks and a Wren,
Have all built their nests in my beard!"

There was a Young Lady whose Nose
Continually prospers and grows;
    When it grew out of sight,
    She exclaimed in a fright
"Oh! Farewell to the end of my Nose!"

---

induced: caused
relinquished: gave up
prospers: does well; flourishes

A Little Nash Menagerie

poems by Ogden Nash

The Kitten

The trouble with a kitten is
THAT
Eventually it becomes a
CAT.

The Fly

The Lord in his wisdom made the fly
And then forgot to tell us why.

The Eel

I don't mind eels
Except as meals.
And the way they feels.

The Octopus

Tell me, O Octopus, I begs,
Is those things arms, or is they legs?
I marvel at thee, Octopus;
If I were thou, I'd call me Us.

---

menagerie: a collection of animals

THE LAMA

The one-l lama,
He's a priest,
The two-l llama,
He's a beast.
And I will bet
A silk pyjama
There isn't any
Three-l lllama.

THE PANTHER

The panther is like a leopard,
Except it hasn't been peppered,
Should you behold a panther crouch,
Prepare to say Ouch.
Better yet, if called by a panther,
Don't anther.

THE JELLYFISH

Who wants my jellyfish?
I'm not sellyfish.

INDEX OF AUTHORS AND TITLES

Acknowledgments

Poems

"The Black Snake" by Patricia Hubbell, From 8 A.M. SHADOWS by Patricia Hubbell. Copyright © 1965, 1993 by Patricia Hubbell. Used by permission of Marian Reiner for the author.

"The Eel," "The Fly," "The Jellyfish," "The Kitten," "The Llama," "The Octopus," and "The Panther" by Ogden Nash. Copyright © 1942, 1942, 1942, 1940, 1931, 1942, 1940 by Ogden Nash. Reprinted by permission of Curtis Brown, Ltd.

"The Naming of Cats" and "The Rum Tum Tugger" from OLD POSSUM'S BOOK OF PRACTICAL CATS, copyright 1939 by T. S. Eliot and renewed 1967 by Esme Valerie Eliot, reprinted by permission of Harcourt, Inc.

"Ode to Mi Gato" by Gary Soto from NEIGHBORHOOD ODES, copyright © 1992 by Gary Soto, reprinted by permission of Harcourt, Inc.

"The Open Door" and "Swift Things Are Beautiful" by Elizabeth Coatsworth, reprinted by permission of Paterson Marsh Ltd. on behalf of the estate of Elizabeth Coatsworth.

"The Pasture" from THE POETRY OF ROBERT FROST edited by Edward Connery Lathem. Copyright 1939, 1967, © 1969 by Henry Holt and Co. Reprinted by permission of Henry Holt and Company, LLC.

Six Haiku from CRICKET SONGS: JAPANESE HAIKU translated or written by Harry Behn. Copyright © 1964 by Harry Behn, copyright renewed 1992 by Prescott Behn, Pamela Behn Adam and Peter Behn. Used by permission of Marian Reiner.

"Something Told the Wild Geese" by Rachel Field from POEMS by Rachel Field. Copyright © 1934 Macmillan Publishing Company; copyright renewed © 1962 by Arthur S. Pederson. Reprinted by permission of Simon and Schuster Books for Young Readers, an imprint of Simon and Schuster Children's Publishing Division.

"The Storm" by Walter de la Mare, reprinted by permission of the Literary Trustees of Walter de la Mare and the Society of Authors as their representative.

"Until I Saw the Sea" by Lilian Moore from I FEEL THE SAME WAY by Lilian Moore. Copyright © 1966, 1967 by Lilian Moore. Used by permission of Marian Reiner for the author.

"Vern" by Gwendolyn Brooks from BRONZEVILLE BOYS AND GIRLS. Reprinted by permission of Brooks Permissions.

"Waiting" by Harry Behn from THE LITTLE RED HILL by Harry Behn. Copyright © 1949 by Harry Behn, copyright renewed 1977 by Alice L. Behn. Used by permission of Marian Reiner.

Stories

"The Bracelet" by Yoshiko Uchida. Copyright © 1976. Reprinted by permission of the Bancroft Library.

"The Circuit" by Francisco Jiménez. Reprinted from *Arizona Quarterly* 28 (1972) by permission of Francisco Jiménez.

"The Dog of Pompeii" by Louis Untermeyer from THE DONKEY GOD by Louis Untermeyer (Harcourt Brace & Company, copyright 1932). Published by arrangement with the Estate of Louis Untermeyer, Norma Anchin Untermeyer c/o Professional Publishing Services Company. This permission is expressly granted by Laurence S. Untermeyer.

"A Just Judge" from FABLES AND FAIRY TALES by Leo Tolstoy, translated by Ann Dunnigan, copyright © 1962 by Ann Dunnigan. Used by permission of Dutton Signet, a division of Penguin Group (USA) Inc.

"Kaddo's Wall" from THE COW-TAIL SWITCH AND OTHER WEST AFRICAN STORIES by Harold Courlander and George Herzog. Copyright 1947, © 1974 by Harold Courlander. Reprinted by permission of Henry Holt and Company, LLC.

"Ooka and the Honest Thief" by I. G. Edmonds, © 1961 by I. G. Edmonds. Reprinted by permission of Scott Meredith Literary Agency

"The Stone" from THE FOUNDLING AND OTHER TALES OF PRYDAIN by Lloyd Alexander. Copyright © 1973 by Lloyd Alexander. Reprinted by permission of Henry Holt and Company, LLC.

"Stray" by Cynthia Rylant from EVERY LIVING THING by Cynthia Rylant, copyright © 1985 by Cynthia Rylant, reprinted by permission of Simon and Schuster Books for Young Readers, an imprint of Simon and Schuster Children's Publishing Division.

"Thank You, M'am" from SHORT STORIES by Langston Hughes. Copyright © 1996 by Ramona Bass and Arnold Rampersad. Reprinted by permission of Hill and Wang, a division of Farrar, Strauss, and Giroux, LLC.

"Zlateh the Goat" from STORIES FOR CHILDREN by Isaac Bashevis Singer. Copyright © 1984 by Isaac Bashevis Singer. Reprinted by permission of Farrar, Strauss, and Giroux, LLC.

Illustrations

Page 112, Raphael: © Hulton/Archive by Getty Images

Page 115, Beethoven, M. Rodig: © Bettmann/Corbis

Page 122, *Little Girl in a Blue Armchair*, Mary Cassatt: Collection of Mr. and Mrs. Paul Mellon, Image © 2003 Board of Trustees, National Gallery of Art, Washington